Magnet

New work from North East writers

New Writing North

Published by New Writing North, 2005

New Writing North
2 School Lane
Whickham
Newcastle upon Tyne
NE16 4SL

New Writing North Limited 3166037
Registered charity number 1062729

ISBN 0-9541456-5-8

Editor: Claire Malcolm
Publications manager: John Adair
Copy editor: Will Mackie
Cover photograph: Sharon Bailey
Cover design: Sumo
Printed by Cromwell Press

New Writing North is the writing development agency for the north east of England. We aim to create an environment in the North East in which new writing in all genres can flourish and develop. We are a unique organisation within the UK, merging as we do individual development work with writers across all media with educational work and the production of creative projects. We work with writers from different genres and forms to develop career opportunities, new commissions, projects, residencies, publications and live events.

www.newwritingnorth.com
www.literaturenortheast.co.uk
www.nr-foundationwriters.com
www.wordmavericks.com

Introduction

The *Magnetic North* programme of live literature began in 2003 with a
series of events which took place at Newcastle Library and Live
Theatre on Newcastle's Quayside. The events programme aimed
to promote regional writing and experiment with presenting live
work via the commissioning of new work for performance. We
wanted audiences to move beyond seeing writers reading from their
new novels or collections of poetry and to give writers the chance to
respond to commissions and to produce work written to be read to a
live audience. Throughout the programme we were able to set writers
specific challenges – to write about a season, be inspired by a song or
get up to some 'rural mischief'; and push them to respond to the
places that they were exploring internationally. In the book you will
find poems and stories inspired by visits to Moscow and Sofia, as
writers explore their responses to these new places.

Also collected in this volume are five stories which were originally
commissioned and published as part of an art book, *Bound*, in 2004.
The stories were inspired by County Durham and Sunderland and all
have a fantastic sense of place.

Claire Malcolm, New Writing North
Autumn 2005

Contents

Writers in Transit

Small Things

Rural Mischief

Poetry for the Season

It Started with a Song

Bound: County Durham stories

About the writers

Writers in Transit

The writers featured in this section were commissioned to produce new work in response to creative visits to Moscow, Russia and Sofia, Bulgaria.

An Expedition to the Taiga

By Andrew Crumey

With thanks to Peter Aleshkovsky

In Moscow, Roy Jones was due to attend a conference of mechanical engineers. Arriving at the airport, he passed through the customs channel and emerged to see a row of impoverished-looking taxi drivers, mournfully waiting in the foyer for their pre-booked customers.

Russia, his wife had warned him, is a wild and unruly place. The taxi drivers are in some instances muggers in disguise. She'd seen it on a TV documentary. They lure rich Westerners into their cars, drive them to remote and shabby neighbourhoods, then allow their passengers to escape with their lives only if they first hand over their every valuable. Even their Polartec fleeces.

But among the drivers Roy Jones saw as he emerged stood one, sallow-faced in a fur hat and battered black leather jacket, bearing a sign saying 'Mr Jones'. How reassuring. Though surely the conference organisers should have remembered that Roy Jones was Dr, not Mr.

They went outside to a grimy white car. Roy Jones felt brave enough to place himself in the passenger seat, holding his briefcase, while the driver casually fitted the larger suitcase into the boot. Roy Jones had just about figured out the seat belt when the driver got in beside him and started the car.

'Do you know where you're going?' Roy Jones asked.

The driver gave a thin smile. 'Yes. Do you?'

Roy Jones didn't know the name of the hotel. The conference organiser had e-mailed it to him last week, but it was a funny Russian word that meant nothing to him: a possible hotel, nothing more. Now the driver was taking him there.

Roy Jones watched the unfolding succession of slab-like buildings and strangely quiet roads, punctuated by advertising hoardings whose enthusiasm was almost touching in its futility. The sky was grey and overcast; the air was filled with swirling powder-snow, whipped by the slipstreams of the ancient, fuming lorries they overtook.

'Do you live in Moscow?' Roy Jones asked. It was all the small-talk he could think of. Long silences were as discomforting to him, even with insignificant foreigners, as long periods without going to the bathroom.

The driver nodded. 'I live in Moscow,' he said. 'All my life, I live in Moscow. Except for one year, I live in London.'

So when he said he lived all his life in Moscow, Roy Jones reasoned, the driver was in fact lying. It was good for Roy Jones to know exactly where he stood. Or rather, sat, with his briefcase clutched tightly on his lap.

'What were you doing in London?' Roy Jones asked.

'A girl,' said the driver enigmatically. He looked the kind of man no woman could ever fall for. At least, no woman that Roy Jones could think of. Like his wife, for instance. Or Dorothy, the departmental secretary at the university. But what about the students? Those female ones, who'd sit on the lawn beneath his office window in the summer term? Roy Jones knew nothing about those young and dangerously carefree girls. None of them were engineers.

'I love London,' said the driver, turning towards Roy Jones with a sudden obliviousness to the road ahead. 'And I hate it.'

It must be a Russian thing, Roy Jones decided: this tendency towards inconsistency. Not to mention a tendency to ignore the road. He said, 'Do you love Moscow, or do you hate it?'

The driver nodded. 'Yes. That's it exactly, my friend.'

The car took a bend, and a dignified building appeared on their left, adorned with a hammer and sickle. Roy Jones thought they would have got rid of all that, but apparently not.

'What I really love,' said the driver, 'is the taiga.'

Roy Jones was puzzled. 'You love the tiger?'

The driver nodded.

'Which tiger is that?'

'The taiga,' the driver repeated. 'You know, the forest.'

From the depths of his memory, Roy Jones recalled a wildlife programme he'd watched one Sunday evening with his wife. The taiga: T-A-I-G-A. A great expanse of forest, between grassy steppe to the south and frozen tundra to the north. So at once, Roy Jones knew exactly where he was with the driver. Lots and lots of trees, the odd bear or eagle, and the soothing voice of David Attenborough, while his wife got up and asked if he wanted more tea.

13

'Of course, the taiga,' said Roy Jones. 'Well, I'm sure it must be very nice. A bit like the New Forest, perhaps?'

'I hate it,' said the driver. 'The taiga; it is beautiful, and it is hell.'

Roy Jones could not recall, in at least twenty years of attendance at international conferences on industrial lubricants, any conversation with a local taxi driver quite like the one that was now evolving. 'Tell me,' he said, 'have you always been a taxi driver?'

His companion shook his head. 'I am not a taxi driver.' Roy Jones felt a shiver of fear; was this the moment when the hidden plan would make itself known, as the driver pulled up in a side street far from any hotel or officer of the local law?

The driver repeated. 'I am not a driver, not a teacher, not a husband, not a writer.' Roy Jones was struggling to find the point of all these negatives. Apart from husband and teacher (or rather, lecturer), Roy Jones was none of these things either. 'No,' said the driver. 'I am a man. That is all I am. You go to taiga, you find this for yourself. You find what you are. Then perhaps you love yourself. Or perhaps you hate.'

'I see,' said Roy Jones. Clearly this taiga place wasn't like the New Forest after all. 'Do you go there often?'

'Not for many years,' said the driver sorrowfully. 'Last time, it was enough for me.' Still the car followed its steady route through streets Roy Jones began to notice less and less, intrigued instead by the driver's words.

'Twelve years ago,' the driver said, 'or maybe more, I can't remember. My cousin and I, we like to hunt. We go to the taiga with our rifles. The big black bird, what do you call it?'

'Crow?'

'No.'

'Eagle?'

'No, big black bird, a kind of grouse. What beautiful meat! And the one with the tail like this...' the driver drew a curve with his finger.

'Lyrebird?'

'Of course not.'

Roy Jones had seen lyrebirds on David Attenborough, but obviously it wasn't taiga week then.

The driver drew the bird's tail again, this time taking both hands from the wheel in order to express himself more accurately, and Roy

Jones realised that his life possibly depended right now on his own neglected skills in ornithology.

'Quail? Ptarmigan?'

'No, no. Quail is with the feathers on his head...' The driver was more interested in doing bird impressions than in watching Moscow traffic. Roy Jones was shrinking into his seat, wondering if his brief-case would have the protective qualities of an airbag, as random bird names continued to spill from his mind.

'Partridge?'

'Yes! Yes!' The driver clapped and gripped the wheel once more. Roy Jones breathed a sigh of relief. A partridge had saved his life.

'That's a good bird,' said the driver. 'We hunt it, in the taiga. And another one...'

'Alright, never mind,' said Roy Jones.

The driver was hurt. 'I bore you?'

Roy Jones was sheepish. For all his consumptive appearance, the driver could still probably kick the shit out of him if he cared to, judging by the deft way he'd handled Roy Jones's suitcase. 'I only meant to ask you what else you hunted. Bears?'

The driver shook his head. 'Bears, you leave them alone, they leave you. But the pig, with the tusks...'

'Wild boar?' Roy Jones said it swiftly, before the driver could bring his hands up and make little tusks out of them that would have sent the car careering off the road into what Roy Jones noticed to be a passing McDonald's.

'Yes, the wild boar. We shot one, cooked it on a fire.'

'That's most interesting,' Roy Jones said politely. 'And you're allowed to light fires in the taiga?' Yes, it really wasn't like the New Forest at all.

'You're allowed to do whatever you want,' said the driver. 'In the taiga, no one can see you. In the taiga, nearest village is maybe a thousand kilometres away. You see another man in the taiga, first thing you do, you reach for your rifle.'

Roy Jones swallowed. 'Well. Fascinating. And you went there with your cousin?'

The driver nodded. 'We camp; we stay in huts. They open all the time; if nobody there you go in, light the fire, live there as long as you want.'

'And if somebody's in the hut when you arrive?'

'Then you no go near. You keep your rifle close by your side.'

All in all, this taiga place sounded a lot less inviting than when David Attenborough did it on the television. Roy Jones's wife had made a fresh pot of tea, and there on the screen was a big cuddly bear, reaching into a tree and mucking up a beehive, just like an outsized Winnie the Pooh. 'Come and look at this, dear,' Roy Jones called to his wife in the kitchen, as the bear slopped bee-studded honey into its hungry mouth. 'Really, these creatures are so comical, don't you think?'

But now the driver had totally spoiled it all. The taiga, it seemed, was just as lawless as the rest of this huge, unfathomable country.

'We go in boat,' he explained.

'You and your cousin?'

The driver nodded. 'Some supplies, essential things. Our rifles, of course. We go up the river, two hundred kilometres from road where we leave the car. Takes us a few days. We hear there's good place for the... for the...'

'Partridges? Grouse?'

'No, the black one. Never mind. We hear there's a hut, nobody is there probably. So, on the third day, we wake up in our tent, wash ourselves in the river, we have some fish to eat. In the taiga, very good fish.'

Roy Jones could almost see it: the smouldering campfire beside the broad, cool waters. And all around, nothing but trees, impenetrably dense.

'We get the boat ready, and my cousin, he say to me suddenly, did you hear that? What? I say. A noise, he tell me. Sound like a gun. I say to him, I hear nothing - you hear a branch breaking. It might be a bear, he say, we better be careful, and I say, never mind about the bear, we make the boat ready, we go to the hut today and we find a nice bed tonight, have everything we need. He laugh - everything except a woman of course. Yes, in the taiga you have everything except that.'

Roy Jones could at least relate to this aspect of the adventure. While the resemblance with the New Forest had dwindled out of existence, the taiga nevertheless had something in common with the field of international tribology research.

'My cousin, he say, let's check the rifles. He not like the sound he heard. In the taiga, you meet another man, he's either mad or he's escaped from a prison.'

'What about you two?'

'We were hunters. That's the other kind you meet. And hunters, they like to hunt. So you not want to meet other hunter. Otherwise, maybe he hunt you.'

The driver slowed up, but it was not a hotel they had arrived at, only a set of traffic lights that soon changed.

'Well, we check the rifles, we get the boat ready, we set off. Beautiful morning. In the taiga, clear days like you see nowhere else. The air is like... like...' Roy Jones quietly prayed that the fresh air of the taiga bore no resemblance to anything that would mean the driver lifting his hands from the wheel again. 'Like honey,' he said at last. 'Air like honey.' All ready for a big bear to come and steal, and without signalling, the driver took a sudden left in front of an oncoming lorry. Roy Jones braced himself, but the taxi easily avoided the approaching vehicle, whose horn blared as they left it rushing behind them.

'And the water,' the driver continued, 'it's like glass. Only few small waves on the wide river, it flows so slow. And the boat cutting through when we start the engine.' He breathed in, as if tasting the honeyed air of the taiga; Roy Jones watched the driver breathe deeply, exhaling noisily before repeating the gesture, and then finally the driver's sickly face darkened. 'Shit!' he murmured. 'The air, to me, it's like a shit.'

Roy Jones wasn't sure if this was Russian contradiction again, or else a comparison between the taiga and the city; but he didn't really care. 'Then you took the boat to the hut?' he said, wishing to move things along to their conclusion, as if this might somehow bring them more quickly to his hotel.

The driver slowly shook his head. 'No,' he said. 'We not make it to the hut. We not make it any place. The boat, it goes fine, engine run smoothly, and then my cousin, he says suddenly: Listen! So I listened, and I hear nothing. My cousin, he leans towards me in the boat, he says, it was another gunshot, you didn't hear it? Me, I reckon he's dreaming. But then, across the water, in front of the boat, there it was: pat-pat-pat-pat-pat!' The driver, using only one hand, made a motion like a flat stone skimming over the waves.

'My cousin, he get hold of me while I watch, he grab me and pull me down in the boat. I raise my head to look, and there it is again, in front of us: pat-pat-pat-pat-pat! Line of bullets hitting the water. A machine gun. Some guys in trees, they want a little fun, little sport. Maybe they sink the boat first, then they kill us. Or else they want the boat. My cousin and me, we're lying in the boat, terrified, and we hear bullets flying over our head: zip-zip-zip-zip!' A zooming finger illustrated this new torment for the benefit of Roy Jones. 'We not steering the boat – I try to hold with my foot. And then: kaa-kaa-kaa-kaa-kaa! Little pieces of wood splinters all over us – a line of holes in the side of the boat. They getting serious. My cousin, he say to me: we gotta do something! And he reach the... the... what do you call the handle on motor you steer with?'

Roy Jones couldn't remember. 'The rudder?'

'No, not rudder I think.'

'Let's just call it the handle,' Roy Jones suggested. 'Tell me what happened next.'

'My cousin, he get the handle between his feet and he go THIS WAY and THIS WAY.' The swerving of the boat was perfectly imitated by the driver's sudden lurching of his body to left and right, some of which was in turn transmitted to the taxi. 'He make the boat spin all around.'

'No need to illustrate,' said Roy Jones. 'I get the idea.'

'And for a moment, I think we gonna turn over in the water, maybe we hide under the boat or something – I dunno, it's crazy, but when a man's firing at you – pa-pa-pa-pa! – you gotta do anything you can. And the boat, it's going everywhere. My cousin can't control it. And then: bang! The boat's grounded at the side of the river. We gotta get out and run for it, while the bullets keep coming at us: za-za-za-za-za-za-za-za! I'm running into the trees, and I see a line of them right beside me, like a rabbit I'm chasing – only I'm the rabbit, and the bullets are chasing me. And I get behind a tree and look round to see the river bank. And there's my cousin lying on the ground, my own cousin in front of my eyes. My poor cousin.'

The driver at this point kissed his fingertips, touched the small faded icon affixed to the car's battered dashboard, and crossed himself.

'Was he dead?' Roy Jones asked. Being a tribologist of international eminence, he was by nature a man of exactitude.

The driver shook his head. 'My cousin not dead. Not quite. His leg was moving – he was trying to push himself along the ground. No bullets now, no sound anywhere, except my cousin, on the ground, trying to get himself to safety, and this kind of gurgling sound he make. Ah – shit!' The driver suddenly stopped the car. 'Here is your hotel.'

Roy Jones looked out and saw a huge building in which, right now, he had absolutely no interest. 'I'd really like to hear the rest of your story,' he said.

The driver glanced at his watch. 'I have another delegate to meet from airport in forty minutes.'

'Well, that gives you plenty of time to get to the end,' Roy Jones suggested; but already the driver had got out and walked round to open the boot. Roy Jones also stepped out of the car, and took charge of the wheeled suitcase that was handed to him. The cab had been arranged by the conference organisers; there was nothing to pay, no more to be said. During much of the preceding story about the taiga, Roy Jones had been quietly wondering whether a tip would be expected; but he had no Russian money, and it seemed that this little episode was about to end and be forgotten – as such episodes always are – without any further resolution.

However, with a sudden burst of initiative, Roy Jones said, 'Do you think you could help me inside with the suitcase?' The driver looked sceptical. Roy Jones said, 'I could even buy you a drink.'

'A drink?'

'Well, a coffee, I suppose. And you could tell me a little more about the taiga.'

The driver smiled. 'I help you then,' he said, taking the suitcase by the carrying handle on its long side, rather than the extendable one for those weedier travellers such as Roy Jones who rely on trolley wheels, and the driver ascended the hotel steps, easily bearing the suitcase while Roy Jones made do with his briefcase, which contained the precious presentation – 'Mixed-phase lubricants: a top-down approach' – that was still his reason for being here, and almost entirely the reason why he left the driver settling comfortably in the hotel bar while he went to check in.

The girl behind the desk was perfectly groomed, but imperfectly trained. It all took a lot longer than Roy Jones would have preferred, and as he handed over his passport, he looked at his watch, wondering if it had really been such a good idea to invite the driver in. Roy Jones was a sucker for a good story, that was his problem. He was simply too impulsive, as his wife told him the other week when he suddenly changed the habit of a lifetime and decided that their next car would not be a Rover after all.

'Enjoy your stay,' the desk girl finally announced with a smile that clearly had had too much prior use. Roy Jones took his key and his luggage and went straight back to the bar, where the driver was sitting silently over a cup of coffee. Roy Jones sat down opposite him at the small wooden table and thought it best to get to the point.

'What did you do about your cousin?' Roy Jones asked.

'What would any man do?' said the driver with a shrug. 'He was lying there in the dirt, trailing blood as he pushed himself along the ground with one foot, trying to reach the trees. At the other side of the river, a man with a machine gun, or two men, or a whole army, were waiting for me to make my move. As soon as I ran out to save my cousin, they would finish both of us.'

'I see,' said Roy Jones. Put in such straightforward terms, the whole matter became as clear as the most elementary problem of engineering. 'So you left your cousin to die?'

The driver's eyebrows shot up. 'To die! You think I'm a monster! No, I never leave any man to die. I take a deep breath, I say a prayer, I kiss the picture of my mother I carry here in my own head, and then I run – yes, I run out from behind the tree, faster than ever I run in my life. And the bullets, they come BA! BA! BA! BA! BA! BA!' The driver's hand chopped salami slices across the table, so loudly that heads turned in response. 'The bullets tear the sleeves of my coat, they chew the leather of my boots. BA! BA! BA! BA! BA! BA! They rip my cousin's back to pieces, and right before my eyes his head explodes – SHAAH!'

Roy Jones gave a jump, and clutched the room key in his hand.

'My cousin, there was no hope. And I never make it back to the trees. So I run to the boat in the water, I jump inside the boat, and the bullets are like crazy. And in all those thousand bullets, not one of them hits my body. I think to myself, I am like a saint. God has chosen this. As many bullets as there are leaves on a tree, as many bullets as there are trees in the forest. They've torn my sleeve, my boot. But not my flesh. And I throw myself in the boat – they can perhaps even see me there, but it was the closest place, closer than the trees where I was already safe. I land in the boat, and my head, it hits the wooden seat, real hard. So here I am, a bullet-proof saint. And a piece of wood knocks me unconscious.'

The driver raised his coffee cup and took a sip. 'How long I lie there? I don't know: a minute, an hour, a day. Next thing, I realise I'm awake, and there's no shooting. They must have decided I was dead. No guns anywhere, except the two loaded rifles lying right beside me in the boat. I wake up, and I remember that my cousin is lying dead. I can't raise my head to look: I can't risk it. Perhaps only a minute has passed since I landed here – who knows? So I lie and wait. All I hear is the gentle wind in the trees, the river lapping against the boat, sometimes the birds. And then, after a while, I hear another boat, far away. I hear a motorboat, slowly it get louder, nearer. And now I know what happens. They come to see what they done. They find me, they shoot me – how can I play dead, when they go through my pockets looking for my wallet? How can I lie still, with my heart pounding and not a drop of blood on my body? I think to myself, this is the final test. I hear the motorboat getting closer, and I reach for the rifles, very slowly. I'm working it out in my head: one rifle or two? And I figure, I start with two, then I drop one when I got something to aim at. First, I'll get up and fire both of them at once, blindly. At least, if nothing else, I'll die shooting.'

The driver drained his cup and stared into it. 'Now perhaps a little vodka, my friend?'

'For you? But you're driving.'

'Only a little one,' he said soothingly. 'And I have some mints that will clear my breath before I drive, so it's OK.' He looked round towards the barman and called out his order, then said to Roy Jones, 'The other motorboat, it's so near now. I hear the motor revving down, idling while it steers closer. I hear someone moving in the boat, sounds like someone walking on planks. I reckon any moment I'll hear a splash as he jumps into the shallow water and then it'll be my moment. I wait and then... and then...'

A glass of vodka materialised on the table.

'SPLASH!' the driver cried, instantly getting to his feet and from both arms spraying with imaginary gunfire the hotel bar and the startled, retreating barman. 'GA-GA-GA-GA-GA-GA! And now I could see them, I dropped the rifle in my left hand and took good aim with the one remaining. The man in the water was on his knees – GA! – I finished him. In the boat, a younger man, who was still trying to cock his rifle when I got him – GA! GA! GA!' The driver sat down.

Roy Jones was shaken. 'You killed them both?'

The driver nodded. 'The one in the water, he was face down, his chest caught on stones on the shallow riverbed and his arms and legs swaying like reeds in the current. I went and turned him over, looked at his face. A man in his forties, perhaps. He had no gun. And in the boat, maybe this other one was the first man's son. That boy, I don't know how old. I got him in the face. All they had between them was their two rifles, same as my cousin and me. The boy's was in his hand, where he'd been trying to cock it. The father's rifle was lying with their fishing gear, unloaded. I checked it all afterwards. So you see, these weren't the ones who had fired at me.'

Roy Jones's mouth was hanging open. 'You killed two innocent men!'

The driver nodded. 'And on the riverbank, my cousin lay in a terrible mess. And our boat was ruined by the gunfire. I congratulated myself that at least now I had a usable boat, thanks to the men I shot.'

Roy Jones was horrified. 'But they were innocent men! They were hunters like you, out on a trip.'

The driver again nodded, drained his glass in one shot, exhaled vodka in his breath and said, 'We too, my cousin and me, we were innocent men. But in the taiga, there is no law except survival. When I lay in the boat and heard them coming, what was I supposed to do? Was I to lie there like a frightened doe and let them shoot me dead? Was I supposed to be a good citizen and stand up, raise my arms in the air, and say, kill me now please? No. In the taiga, you live by the law of the taiga. The father and son in the motorboat, they knew that too. Or they should have known. A wild boar, it can kill you. A bear, it can kill you. A damned mushroom, it can kill you. And a man, he will certainly kill you, if he thinks that this is what he has to do. So, my friend, I regret nothing, except that I ran a little too fast towards the trees, like a cotton-assed rabbit, when I should have been saving my cousin. But in the taiga, we are not asked to make choices, only to act.'

It seemed to Roy Jones that the story had now come to its dreadful end. 'What about the ones with the machine gun?'

The driver shrugged. 'They went away. They watched me lying in the boat for an hour or a day, and they got bored. I don't know. Perhaps the father and son really were the killers, and left their machine gun on the opposite bank of the river while they came to take some trophies. Who cares? You kill a bear, you don't go asking afterwards what it had for dinner. You shoot, you kill, you go to sleep and you move on. This is law of the taiga. And you see, my friend, I am a man of the law.'

The driver reached inside his coat. Roy Jones wondered if a gun might emerge, or perhaps a photograph of the lost cousin. It was only a packet of cigarettes that came out, and a cheap lighter. 'Relax,' the driver said with a smile. 'It was all a long time ago.'

'Did you bury those people? Did you tell the police?'

'Relax.' The driver lit a cigarette. 'The dead are in heaven, it's we who have to live on earth. I am a husband, a father. I drive a taxi, I write poetry.'

'You're a poet?'

The driver nodded. 'I've published books, won a few prizes. Perhaps you think I demean my art by driving a taxi. But I have to earn a living. This is law of the city. And I promise you, since the last time in the taiga, I kill no more people.' He chuckled. 'Killing, it's bad for you, like smoking. Too bad I can't give up smoking like the doctor says I should, and the vodka. Doctor says I have a heart attack in next two years. He can see it like a clock. I say to him, OK.' The driver looked down at his empty vodka glass, and the empty cup beside it. 'Thanks,' he said to Roy Jones.

'Like another?'

'No, I die soon enough in any case.' He stood up to leave. 'Enjoy your stay,' he said to Roy Jones. The two men shook hands, then the taxi driver walked briskly across the hotel foyer, giving a final friendly wave before disappearing out through the heavy revolving door.

Two hours later, Roy Jones was in his room, showered, changed and sufficiently refreshed to begin the next part of the day. It was still only lunchtime: he understood that he was due to be collected by someone from the conference, who would presumably also take care of feeding him. He was at the mercy of whoever should happen to appear.

The telephone rang. Roy Jones went to the chipped wooden desk where it sat, and lifted the receiver.

'Mr Jones?'

'Speaking.'

'I am here to take you to the conference.'

'Splendid.'

'You had a safe trip?'

'Absolutely.'

'Good. Please be in the foyer in five minutes.'

'Of course.' Roy Jones hung up. His briefcase was ready, and he checked once again that the text of 'Mixed-phase lubricants: a top-down approach' was safely stored there. He put on his coat, then took the elevator to the lobby, where a man in a long grey coat paced conspicuously to and fro.

'I'm Dr Jones.' He reached out his hand for the other to shake.

'Hello, sir. Now let us go.' And he led Roy Jones outside to his car.

This was to be a journey of the strictly no-nonsense kind, in contrast to the earlier taxi ride. Attempting to make conversation out of his habitual sense of politeness, Roy Jones asked, 'Are you a tribologist yourself?' The driver merely gave him a look of incomprehension, remaining silent until they reached their destination.

'Here is conference centre,' said the driver, suddenly pulling up. They both got out, and Roy Jones followed him inside. Everything seemed so colourless in comparison with the earlier taxi driver's story of the taiga. That alone had been real: the wrong men, shot innocently for daring to approach a man's boat.

Roy Jones followed his escort upstairs, where he was deposited at a desk whose occupant smiled and gave him a badge with his name on it: Mr N Jones. They hadn't even got his initial right this time, never mind his title. A bearded man came over, and the next thing Roy Jones knew, he was being shaken by the hand; embraced, even.

'It is so good to meet you, Mr Jones. We are delighted that you will be speaking at the seminar – and you are just in time! We were a little nervous that you would not be here!'

Roy Jones's stomach rumbled as he was swiftly introduced to four or five people whose names came from the impenetrably unmemorable world of Tolstoy. One was a woman whose handshake was like touching polished ivory, and whose eyes curved and slanted like a message from a distant wilderness. She certainly didn't look like your average tribologist.

Barely able to take in his surroundings, Roy Jones was then escorted to the seminar room, where rows of chairs, mostly filled, faced a desk with a microphone on it, and an empty seat behind. This was where he was led, and as Roy Jones sat down, it occurred to him that it was just as well he'd brought a print-out of his talk as well as the PowerPoint file, since there wasn't an overhead machine in sight.

And so there he was at last, sitting with the text laid neatly before him, ready to embark on a voyage of discovery through the multifaceted world of mixed-phase lubricants. His bearded host intended first to say a few words in Russian. Some of the audience members, Roy Jones now observed, were wearing headsets, of the kind a diplomat might sport in a United Nations debate. There was one lying on Roy Jones's desk; and at the back of the room, he could see a welldressed woman neatly encased in a glass-walled booth, whose role was evidently that of interpreter. Roy Jones put on his headset, and immediately heard the woman's smooth, authoritative voice as she translated what the Russian was saying.

'... has done some very significant work, which I have followed with considerable interest. Mr Jones occupies the boundary, I might say, between fantasy and reality: he repeatedly asks us to consider the question, what is true, what is false?'

Roy Jones weighed this comment up, finding a pleasing balance between flattery and accuracy. Yes; his work on mixed-phase lubricants had questioned some of the most familiar assumptions of the subject.

'And Mr Jones has developed a system of ideas that are in some ways challenging. When he says, for example, "The greatest adventure we can undertake is to cease to be ourself" I understand here something we find also in Chekhov...'

What the devil did that mean? When did Roy Jones ever say that?

'In his most recent book, *The Truth About My Wife*, Neville Jones exposes the dilemma of people trapped by convention, who long to live a more spiritual life, but can find this only through the most terrible acts of depravity...'

Suddenly it all began to make terrible sense to Dr Roy Jones, tribologist. Listening to the translated words of the portly, bearded intellectual as he described the literary works of Neville Jones, novelist, his hapless namesake realised why the audience so little resembled the international congregations of engineers whom it was his life's work to address, and with luck to impress. This array of Russian poets, dramatists, literary critics and assorted book-lovers hadn't come here to listen to a story about forces in mixed-phase fluids. And somewhere, in some other conference centre in Moscow right now, a poor bastard called Neville Jones was being introduced to a bunch of structural scientists, having made the same mistake as Roy when he got off the plane and saw a taxi driver holding a sign reading 'Mr Jones'. This great writer – winner of all sorts of prizes, according to the introduction now being offered in his absence – was the other half of a glorious mix-up, and now would be preparing to sell his wares to an assembly of engineers. Would he pull it off? Would he be able to stand up in the boat with a gun in each hand and save the day?

Roy Jones would. With growing confidence, he listened to the eulogy being offered him. He was wise, far-sighted, profound in moral perception, deft in linguistic invention. He was shocking, at times even disgusting; yet always pure. And above all, said his host, invariably surprising. Yes, he'd surprise them all right.

The audience were applauding. The bearded intellectual had said enough about the glory and importance of Neville Jones. Now it was Roy's turn to preserve the reputation of his ancient tribe. All fell silent: the interpreter was waiting for his words, ready to convey them in Russian to those unable to comprehend him directly.

'Ladies and gentlemen,' he began. 'I want to tell you a story. It's up to you whether or not you want to believe it. Some years ago, my cousin and I went on an expedition to the taiga...'

Proposal for a Monument to the Third International

By Sean O'Brien

'All that is solid melts into air'
The Communist Manifesto

SOLO
I was dreaming in a station of the Metro.
The railbeds were freezing rivers of blood
With bergs of fat, where millions knelt
To eat and drink,

CHORUS
                    and it was good.

SOLO
What are they singing,

CHORUS
                    the crowd

SOLO
That is never the same from moment to moment,

CHORUS
The crowd

SOLO
            whose faces vanish
And re-form, that have no names,

CHORUS
The crowd with its mouthful of blood,
The crowd

27

SOLO
>   In which the million you and I are lost
Like information buried in an archive?
What is that song?

CHORUS
We are buried alive.
We are not what was meant.
Let history finish.
Let stones become stars. Let the stars speak.

SOLO
Let those inside the walls of adamantine
Ice-cream reply in a deafening whisper
As ice writes its name in the river again.
History, history, what are our names?

Little sister, tell me, can you see
Hosts of steam-angels, racing away
Down the blue Moskva at wavetop height
To confer their industrial blessings
On fur and glass, on felt and skin
And the old man who wearily enters
The forest of coats at the end of the day
To come back with ours? Likewise the babushka
Sweeping dead steam from the underpass
Is blessed and when the state withers will stand
With her brothers and sisters
On the wintry glacis by the Kremlin wall
By the site of executions.

CHORUS
The city runs like science fiction backwards.
Putin in his sheet-steel chariot
Is brandishing a grail of blood and vlaast
On a stem of twisted dragon-tails.

SOLO
I rode to the twenty-ninth floor
Of the Hotel Ukraina, then climbed the last steps
To the last locked room
Where a camera obscura portrayed the night city
As Stalin might dream it himself
From one of the seven dark stars he cast
So high that the heavens themselves
Were extinguished.

I turned to descend and there by the door
Was a wizened old man, sitting smoking.
A red fire-bucket was full of his ash.
He wore two watches and between his eyes
A bullet hole.
He looked indifferently through me.
Brothers, this is all I can recall.

CHORUS
The Tambov wolf shall be your comrade now
This is your station now.
Press to the doors.

SOLO
Let us walk over the bridge
By the pool where the steam-angels
Spend their retirement.
Let us walk over the snow
In the field of dead statues.

We shall hand in our coats
To the dear old dead couple
Who add our black coats to the forest of coats
In the province of coats
And the bear Mikhail Semyonov
Presides in the court of the coats this day.

Shall we go in
And look at the art?

CHORUS
Up here is the modest proposal
A tower
A furnace
A children's amusement
Babel
And the key to all economies
When Eiffel took a potion he made this.

SOLO
What is it made of?

CHORUS
Of matchwood and wire
Brown paper and misunderstanding.
This is no longer historical.
Art
And no longer historical,
Art
And can never remember the time.

SOLO
What does it tell us?

CHORUS
Oh, nothing.

SOLO
What shall we hope for?

CHORUS
To come here and see.
To have your curious half hour.
To go back through the crowd,

SOLO
To take our coats from the forest of coats
And tip the babushka

And walk to the Metro
And stand in the crowd between trains
When the blood is not running.

CHORUS
To know
We are buried alive,
To know
We are not what was meant.
Let history finish.
Let stones become stars
And let the stars speak.

Esperanto Anonyme

By Mark Robinson

For Bill Herbert, il lista-creatore migliore

Esperanto na billiardo
Esperanto de statistico
Esperanto of CNN
Esperanto of Chelski and Arsenal
Esperanto ah morning coughs
Esperanto of showerheads
Esperanto da breakfast buffet
Esperanto di bus
Esperanto of football stadia
Esperanto ye barking dogs
Esperanto a empty buzzwords
Esperanto na dead paradigms
Esperanto o't smoking gun
Esperanto of silence
Esperanto di iambs
Esperanto na ragged dance
Esperanto von fear
Esperanto o panic
Esperanto da drum and basics
Esperanto a hips
Esperanto na breath
Esperanto di grafiti
Esperanto de puzzled brows
Esperanto na hope
Esperanto ov hope over experience
Esperanto of beer
Esperanto of lists

Going

By Mark Robinson

I recall it now as it will be then:
stillness suddenly present overhead
and the earth twitching madly beneath my feet,
a Thursday beaten with sticks and sickly sweet.

I will leave behind a half hummable tune,
and messages etched in the soles of my shoes.
Brickwork kicked into chunks by the gate
suggest what happened happened too late.

A Thursday when dark fades in before three,
still years from a breath of the weekend,
I will go, eyes open, not awash with pain,
but wanting them to wish I crop up again.

It will rain as they wake to how I'm not there,
as train-rattle piles through the evening air
that holds my silence and stills my tongue
as our garden fills and swells with its song.

How I Learned to Sing

By Mark Robinson

The day spins like a plate on a pole,
sunlight streaming down and around us,
carving shadows out of the beach.
A snag of mishaps has shaped mum's face
into a taut parody of itself.
We are sent to find crabs, in pools
where we have not seen a crab for years.
The sea is a vein in the estuary,
the tide coming in a race memory,
and stranded pools dot the sand
with water still so cold it cramps
our calves before we can fight.
Then my sister is suddenly dancing,
splashing towards me with her discovery,
a small pink starfish she waves
in my dumbstruck face.
Though she is smaller, I can't reach it,
she ducks and swerves away
like the memory of it now.
I can't reach her, mum and dad
are too far back to help, but
I want that starfish, want to run
my fingers over its serrations,
pop it in my pocket to frighten
my mum with as we wipe sand
from between our toes later.
I start to scream at my sister,
first words and then just noises,
and the gulls turn from pencil flicks
to real birds with real blood
rushing beneath sharp feathers,
claws asking my shirt whether
it will rip or be carried off,
and now my voice has gone soft

and crying for what I can't get
I feel my wings rise and set,
the gulls' craws and my own throat
harmonise as I pale and float
up and over the docile waves,
not worrying, or wanting to be saved,
looking down on the strip of beach
at the family I could not reach,
and singing back back back.

Sofia City Blues

By WN Herbert

I am like the toon where I was born,
my heart is always somewhere where it doesnae belong;
the demons of the ages rip my head to rags
and I carry my soul in these three bags,
I carry my soul in these three bags.

do you confuse great pop music
with being in love
well, don't apologise

I'm the less travelled, unravelled man
just a-waitin for a slogan in the New Bedlam
I'm the man outwith the language, wi the slanguage full of baggage
and I carry my soul in these three bags,
I carry my soul in these three bags.

do you peel your mind and find
city within city within city?
don't make a career out of it

They tell me stop translatin and enjoy the kitsch
beginning wi thi wife of Doktor Lachnavitch
but another ladybird just appeared on my pad
she says I carry my soul in these three bags,
I carry my soul in these three bags.

the bed is sandy
the bed is Sunday
the bed is bad lasagne

tissue remains

Tissue Remains

By WN Herbert

Too many hands were pressing on
my breastbone and my brow in
the great marble sandwich of the state museum.
We slid like sliced meat about the Thracian room
filled with so much gold as though
Midas had beaten up a rose garden
into this dinner service full of slurring rhyta*.
The bas-relief horsemen insisted
on cornering their boars with always
one hand flung out behind them
not clutching a spear but letting the reins stream
through their casually tugging long fingers
which would only take a millennium to
rearrange themselves into
the next door icons' serpentine blessing machines.
But for now the faces were Alexander clones
so that was never where my eyes could rest
till the skull-bulb helmets drew us,
their tight-lipped spaces that hold
exact absences, to the case in which
earth-coloured armour propped on perspex shoulders
and shinbones. And the greaves,
that word that's almost a wound,
had their own card that told us
what survives the centuries' ceaseless fingers
is less than the step I couldn't take away:
'Bronze, traces of leather straps, tissue remains.'

*rhyta: drinking-cups

Martenitza

By Andy Croft

Long, long ago, there was a king
　　Who put his foes to flight,
And the victory colours of the Spring
　　Were bannered red and white.

Today the victory of March will thaw
　　The blood that stains the snow,
The hope that Spring will come once more,
　　And the red roses grow.

And the colour of blood is red,
　　And white are the snows that fall,
And despite the blood that kings have shed
　　The Spring belongs to all.

Kartichka ot Sofia

By Andy Croft

Just round the corner from the new hotel
That someone says was built by Russian mafia,
A kind of multi-alphabet dysgraphia
Now flourishes on tree-lined walls which spell
'Red Madness!', 'Lokomotib', 'He Ho HATO',
'bHC,' 'Cockney Sparrers Oi ! Oi ! Oi !',
'CCCP', 'CSKA', 'Destroy!'
Town-planners and utopians since Plato
Have found their well-drawn plans a palimpsest
Through which the scrawl of Babel-tongued graffiti
Can still be read – part threat and part entreaty –
Return of the repressed, in lines addressed
To those who've read the writing on the wall
From those who aren't supposed to write at all.

The Rotunda

By Andy Croft

The woman lights another tapered prayer,
Whose weeping wax now gutters in the gloom,
A ritual which only can illume
A world of superstition and despair.
Above us, in the bright empyrean blue,
A frieze of flaky prophets on the ceiling
Is laced with holes, as if the heavens were peeling
To let the pagan night beneath show through.
Behind each fading fresco lies the next,
Precise as tree-rings, measuring the stages
Of human hope and terror through the ages
Like missing pages in a monkish text.
As if the consolations of such art
Could ever warm this heartless world's cold heart.

The Baron Munchausen Bar, Sofia

By Andy Croft

For Bill

'We drink, we sing with recklessness,
We snarl against the tyrant foe,
The taverns are too small for us,
"To the mountains we shall go."'
H Botev

You follow the yellow-brick road through the snow,
Past the topless young girls on the highway,
Through Horrible Valley and Terrible Pass
Till at last you will come to a doorway.

It's tucked between Schweik's and Flanagan's Bar,
Down a side-street of uneven cobbles,
But once you're inside you know you're with friends
Who will help you forget all your troubles.

Inside it's so crowded and smoky and dark
That you can't tell one hand from the other;
Here a Yes means a No and a No means a Yes,
And the neighbouring sexes mean either.

You hang up your hang ups just inside the door
In exchange for a small token gesture,
Sly Peter will offer to buy you a beer
And ask you to drink to the future.

And after a while you can see that it's full
Of artists in shades and black leather,
Like talking heads chained in the inferno-dark
They talk of new sins and old lovers.

Here the bar-maids are lovely as Catherine the Great,
And the beer tastes as cold as the Iskar;
On TV the football is never nil-nil,
And the Hristos are wrapping up Moskva.

And the peppers are red as CSKA shirts,
And the vegetable soup is near solid
With the flesh of the Chopski, that gentlest of tribes
Who taught us all how to make salad.

Here the regulars vote for a fairy-tale-king,
Who it's rumoured supports Barcelona,
He doesn't like children but comes in to drink
With the tough-looking boys in the corner.

Each night if you want you can drink the bar dry
As long as the Baron has credit,
Though the menu's as large as the Vitosha hills,
The bill is so small you can't read it.

If ever you leave here (and some never do)
You will find that the snow is still falling,
In Batenberg Square they've forgotten the date,
And the frozen tongued bells have stopped pealing;

And the skate-boarders spin round the partisan dead
In the gardens on Boulevard Levski,
And the tomb of Dimitrov's been swapped overnight
For an oversize bottle of whisky;

And the past is as clean as the streets in the snow,
And everyone's tired and sleepy,
And the future's as bright as the man in the moon,
And freedom makes everyone happy;

And the statues outside are stiff with the cold,
And the girls by the road are still topless;
And the children of beggars are sleeping outside,
And the cold constellations are helpless.

The Baron untethers one half of his horse
Which he tied to an Orthodox steeple,
And wishes you all a merry good night
As he flies off to Constantinople.

Some say he's a con-man, some say he's for real,
Some say that the Baron's in earnest,
But don't take my word for it, go there yourself –
You'll never believe it all. Honest.

Sofia Blues

By Fadia Faqir

Dedicated to Nadezhda Radulova, Georgi Gospodinov, Plamen Doynov, Momchil Nikolov, Toma Markov, VBV, Bill Herbert, Mark Robinson, Leah Davcheva, Filipina Filipova and Bluba Lu.

1. Weapons of Mass Destruction

'We found two oranges in your suitcase.
We also found some fresh thyme,
A can of olive oil,
And a packet of ground coffee with cardamom.
We could not find a rosary,
But you must have one in your heart.
Please follow me madam.'

2. The Love of Tortoises

My mother has four tortoises in the flower bed. She cleared some space and made them a make-shift shelter out of bricks and a metal sheet. Every morning, when they hear her footsteps coming down the stairs to the garden, they come out of their shelter and wait to be loved. She would feed them, run her fingers on their leathery shell and talk to them. She said to me once that the little one had a serious fall and one of the squares in his domed shell fell out. 'But I stuck it back with some glue and it worked. His shell is lovely now and you can hardly notice the scar.' When she came to Britain to visit me the tortoises refused to eat. My father tried everything, lettuce, tomatoes, aubergines, potatoes, but the tortoises refused to eat. 'How silly can you be?' my mother said. A week later my father left a message on my answerphone saying, 'They finally called off their hunger strike.' The next day he was arrested.

3. The Caliph Has No Clothes

'Ladies and gentlemen the Caliph has a rare skin condition
That keeps him awake at night.
Indian silk gives him a right rash.
Egyptian cotton makes him itchy like hell.
Anyone who finds a cure
Will be given a hundred gold coins.'
An old woman whispered, 'Sackcloth.'
The Caliph ordered his hangman to chop her head off.
Stark naked, shivering, and raw
He stood on the balcony and watched the beheading.
The funny thing is: sackcloth worked.

Sofia, 2:30am-3:44am
Wednesday, 22 October 2003

4. Iraq

You must not play with the boys in the streets; you are a girl. Smile.
Go to school. Do your homework. Wash behind your ears. Help him
take off his helmet. Unbutton his bullet-proof vest. Undo the laces of
his combat boots. Undress him. Wash him. Give him some food.
Smile. Dance for him. *She is still unripe.* Undress for him. If he touches
your breasts make a nice sound. Open your legs. Let him, let him
out. Let him in, let him out. It does not hurt. Smile. Learn to love
him. *She is still unripe.*
   Through the lattice window I see you push the gate open.
   You walk in: tall, white, unfamiliar, sweaty.
   My father says: '*Dolarayn 'yani kash*' (Two dollars, sir, in cash)
   Do your homework. It does not hurt. Let him in, let him out. Learn
to love him...

Sofia, 11:48pm
Saturday, 25 October 2003

5. Mathematics

In the morning I = 0
Lunch time I = I -
Evening I = serene
Night time I = 0 + fear
I = Arab
No
I = British
No
I = Muslim
No
I = Arab
No
I = British
No, No, No
I + two white men = tentative
Mute
I + two Arab men = honour
I = a Bulgarian man, nearly
I = a Bulgarian woman, almost
I + an Arab man = silent
I + university = speech
I + mosque = sinful
I + church = blasphemy
I = an Arab man - -
An Arab + 9/11 = 0
A woman = - -
I = 0 - -
I + father = female = 0 - -
I + son = female = treason = 0 - -
I + husband = harmony
But I + mother = I + + + +

Durham, 6:30pm
Tuesday, 28 October 2003

Small Things

The poets in this section were commissioned to write new poems for National Poetry Day 2003. The theme we chose was 'small things and small places'. Ellen Phethean and Maureen Almond worked with primary school children and teachers to produce poems for the day.

Small Things in the Cupboards of Long Relationships

By Julia Darling

The foreign coins we didn't spend,
a once-blown whistle, a fairy light,
a photo fallen from a frame,
(you and I, alarmed, in a gondola).

The things between, the useless scrap
in the cupboards of monogamy;
the dice you rolled, a scrabble Z,
lottery tickets that didn't win.

Immaterial, but gathering weight;
a broken chain, a silver pin,
lidless lipsticks, the Queen of Spades,
bent needles, tiny balls of wool.

Gathering in our itching folds,
dropped like cells, discarded skin;
an argument wrapped in a rubber band,
keys that don't fit any lock.

Where will it go, this anti-matter,
When we are gone, our houses cleared,
these broken pens, clips and screws,
a timetable for the midnight train?

That promise in a golden wrapper
a baby's shoe, a box of pain?
It will burn down, to sticky resin
be buried in the earth's sore heart.
To weight the world, and keep it steady
for we held on, and did not part.

The Lost Birds of England

By Julia Darling

I start out large; a flapping bird
on a bike, wide eared and keen,
and the day is an unshaken mat,
the muscles in my shins are tight
I'm in flight. I'm heading west,

past the mouthy dental school
(lost a molar there in 84),
scooting on to Spital Tongues,
to Stanton Street. Men stare from doors,
like I'm a stranger in their town.

Too big, too big. I look unlikely,
striding into **Pasha Fabrics**,
a corner world, of rolls of satin,
embroidered crepe, slidey silk,
a man in grey looks up sideways,

says, 'Winter's coming, close the door.'
'True!' I shout, 'But I'm a poet?
I'm here, I rather like your shop!'
He sinks down lower, peeps, and glowers.
'I know nothing. I'm not talking.'

So that's that. I get the message.
I'm too loud to find the poem.
I tiptoe in to **Sweets of Fenham**,
a cave of bursts, cakes made of jewels:
spun sugar balls, crimson, gold.

A tiny bride and groom hold hands
On the icing top of a high-rise cake.
I buy a bright green square of fudge,
and go and sit on sweet Nun's Moor.
I nibble it, it makes me strong

and smaller too, my wide ears wilt.
I pause outside Bev's fruit and veg
(she once gave me fruit for my baby),
but Bev is gone, and three hard white men
sit grimly amongst plums and grapes.

I'm on the bike and I'm gliding
down Tamworth Road, to Philip Street.
There's a café, with a felt-tip sign,
says *Come In, Make Friends*
So I do, but don't. I order tea.

They give me sugar on a silver spoon.
Christians watch me stirring, sipping,
Watch me looking at Christian menus.
Watch me listening to the radio crooning
I'm Sitting on the Dock of the Bay.

Avoid hyperthermia says a poster.
They point to the clock above my head,
say, *'It's getting dark. Time to close.'*
And I slip out, trying to be smaller,
still too big, still unwieldy.

I'm tired as a lost bird of England
after an international flight.
I know this because I read the label,
In the **Museum For Those Who Are Extinct**
after hours of shrinking, sucking in.

I decreased my scale, left the bike,
I had to, to survive, I learnt
to wriggle from sight, to camouflage.
Stuffed birds are interested in poets,
they look with cocked enquiring heads

and let you share their worms, and nests.
They tell you the details of their births,
their habitats, their tragic ends,
I'm pally with the brown Scops owl,
the blue-cheeked thrush nests in my hair.

I'm with the dear lost birds of England,
and they are small, and so am I.
Like the dotterel, you won't see me,
You might hear me sigh, but by the time
You've pulled out your New Age binoculars

I'll have disappeared, be history.

Triads on Smallness

By Ellen Phethean

Three euphemisms for small:
bijou, tabloid, elegant sufficiency

Three small sizes:
32 double A, a pub measure, a baby carrot

Three small but important dots:
the dot that makes the minim swing, the dot that makes the e-mail more deadly
than the mail, the dot of time

Three small but perfectly formed fruits:
the kumquat, the wild strawberry, the cherry tomato

Three small clichés:
small but perfectly formed, good things come in small packets, well just a
small one then

Three things it's better not to do:
have too many small ones, depend on stilettos, believe in e-mails offering
amplitude

Three communities of size:
the Wee Free, jockeys, the seven dwarves

Three ways of celebrating small:
write poems on Post-Its, carry cocktail parasols, scatter multi-coloured
hundreds and thousands wherever you go

Three petite poetic structures:
triolet, versicle, haiku,

Three great miniatures:
bonsai trees, dolly mixtures, the 2nd Earl of Essex

Three small lies:
You'll grow, size doesn't matter, lots of famous people were small

Three ideas to ponder as you fall asleep:
which famous people were small, why seven dwarves, the nature of relativity

Three small moments in a lifetime:
the sperm meets the egg, the blink of an eye, the last breath

We Are Small

By Hilton School Year 5, with Miss Scott and Ellen Phethean

I'm a grain of sand made from a rock rubbed by the sea over
millions of years. The only thing I know is sea, blue and grey,
and the sound of the waves.

I'm an atom. I live in a cave underground. It's good.

I'm a microchip in a computer. I was made by robots. I do the hard work.

I'm a metal connector in a circuit board, it gets really hot in here.
I was made by the human race.

I'm a speck of dust, I came from something dusty. The wardrobe
is ten feet tall, I will never reach it.

I come from a mouldy plum, squashed in a supermarket. I'm bacterium.

I'm a germ caught off someone else, a swollen gland disease.
My world is red; I hate that heart beating at night I never get to sleep.

I'm a blood cell: I live inside you. When I get old I dissolve
and others replace me.

I'm made from wheat in a field. I'm white and soft, my packet is white.

I'm two long antennae. I hang from an ant's head. Someone stood
on me and I fell off.

I'm a decimal, made from a whole number. My world is inky
I get written down on every kind of paper. I always have a rhythm
in my head. How to multiply and divide is the only thing I know.

I'm a baby's eyelash. I feel the baby flick its eye, it's ticklish.
The mummy's big face looks down, the baby laughs.

I'm a flea from a dog. My world is brown and gold. The only thing I know about is hair.

I'm an ant from a hole in the path. When I go out, I worry because big things pick me up.

I'm a tiny person, I live in a box. I eat biscuit crumbs and drink water.

I'm a Borrower. When I was a baby I slept on a sock. The important thing is surviving.

I'm the cupcake mistaken for a whale: It's important not to get eaten.

I'm a rabbit's ear. I see pink and white, I hear a thousand things.

I'm a head-lice egg, made by two head-lice. Inside my mum's belly it is silent. Once I'm born into the world it starts all over again.

I'm a rabbit's tooth. I come from pink gums. I am the front tooth. I can see perfectly.

I am legs that come from the back end of a guinea pig. You can't move without legs.

I'm a rabbit's nose. It is very cold and very dark around me. I know how to sniff out good and bad food.

I was born as a cat's claw. I kill rats. I live in a rubbish bin, I hear shouting out there in the alley.

I am a baby's hand. My world is cold and damp. I feel bits of food. The biggest thing in my world is my mam.

I came from a bull mastiff's belly with my brothers and sisters. I'm beigey brown with slaver on my cheeks.

I was made by a blue budgie. The important things are my nest in the tree and where my mother is when it's time to go and get worms for dinner.

I was made in a factory. There are lots of bright colours around me. I smell icing and hear the rattling of the other hundreds and thousands around me, but nobody knows me in this tub.

I come from a mine; then they polished me up and put me in a box. I can smell polish. They look like giants. What's important to me is the back of my earring. I'm a diamond ear stud.

Seven From Seven

By Fiona Ritchie Walker

Inspired by the seven cubicles in the ladies' toilets at Newcastle Central Station

I was hoping they'd have a disabled,
something big enough for me and my suitcase.
With Jim, it wasn't a problem, buying coffee
then needing to spend a penny, but I've had to leave
the mug on the counter, fetch my case round,
prop it by the toilet door.
I've pulled the strap through as far as I can,
if someone tries to take it I'll be ready.
My first trip to our Margaret's without him.
I've filled his half with presents for the children.

This is all I need.
You should have asked me, Mummy.
You're a big girl now. Wait until I find
something clean. *But, Mummy*
Get these off.
Mummy, I
It's almost time to get our train.
I like seeing Daddy.
Put your leg through. Quickly.
Mummy, you're hurting.
Those socks will have to do. Don't move.
When can we see Daddy again?
Next time you tell me, OK?
You should have asked me, Mummy.

You wonder if they'd do it on their own.
Wrappers, juice cartons scattered on the floor
and those sinks, four of them full of water.
No-one cares. Plus the tiles, sopping wet.
Someone will take a tumble, mark my words.
At least there's toilet roll, no graffiti either,

but no wonder the country's in the state it's in.
And if they install these stupid button flushes
how can they expect them to work every time,
and me standing waiting for the cistern to refill.
I should have hung on 'til I'd got the Metro home.

It's the kind of purse I'd fancy for myself,
soft leather, with a separate bit for credit cards,
and there it was, peeping from your jacket pocket,
with you so busy wiping away tears,
his arms around your shoulders,
you didn't feel my hand, but then
they never do, so full of their own
kissing and partings, they ignore
the security warnings, which is why
I'm tearing the two of you apart,
scattering you like ashes,
stuffing your student card
into the sanitary disposal unit
trying not to think of the way
he'll hold you close
when you tell him what's happencd.

We like to share,
don't mind the squash.
She holds my bag then I take hers,
we've been doing it for years.
She said she liked my jacket and I knew
by the weekend she'd have one the same
so when I unzipped my jeans and she saw
my Calvin Klein's I couldn't resist.
Doesn't your Alan wear this kind too?
Off she stomped, left the door wide open,
stupid bitch. By the weekend she'll be over it.
We like to share.

There are eight tiles.
Twenty-four if you count the bits round the edges.
There are ten minutes
until the train comes in
and I'm wondering how long it will take
for my eyes to dry,
how long I'll be able to keep smiling,
pretending I'm happy that she's off
somewhere new without me.
I know, we don't own them,
and she's sensible enough, but every time
I think about catching the bus back home
my eyes fill up and I try to think
of something else. One two,
            three, four   five, six,
seven   eight.

An open lipstick rolls under the cubicle wall.
I inch it back towards your outstretched hand.
Your faint *thank you* carries
over the whine of the hand-drier,
an end-of-the-row flush.

Small Things I Have Slept With

By Fiona Ritchie Walker

Inspired by an article on dust mites by Dr Robert Dunn

Today I am a moveable feast, taking my dead skin
to a different bed, depriving
my own dust mites for ten days,
though they won't go hungry.
I've left them a real treat, not changed the sheets.

Even now their mouths are filling up
with skin and sweat shed in restless dreams.
Hunks of me are setting off across the threshold,
I disappear through cracks.

On my organic pillow generations breed and die,
all smaller than the full stop at the end of this line.
No heart or head, they've given up on eyes,
rely on eight hairy legs to travel
between sheets and beyond,
finding new ecosystems. Madonna, the Queen,
the Pope, that street kid on the corner,
each of us on the menu.

Tonight the mites are dining out,
this hotel bed a smorgasbord of nationalities,
my every turn under the covers revealing
potential partners, high with pheromones,
hanging on every fibre.

I wonder if they sleep and do they dream,
imagining themselves in hummingbird nostrils,
riding on the feet of army ants
until my earthquake turnings make their world unsteady.

Feast and enjoy, you skin-seeking arachnids.
This all-you-can-eat-buffet
will be power-showered clean in the morning.

Supporting Roles

By Joan Hewitt

1. Hamlet's Ex-Wife

Your dark combustion of intellect and doubt
stopped me in my tracks.
Ophelia seemed far too listless.
What you needed was a wife
(unshaved, you were even more compelling)
who'd give space to get your act together
and help you face your anger for your mother.

Marriage was perfect for soliloquies.
The whole hullabaloo, the meals,
child-care arrangements, and the deaths
of pets were a backdrop for your isolation
Side-stage even, your chafing shadow
fell across the birthday tea:
the cue for your big speech to no-one
but yourself, when we all went silent.

In the end, I told you, either top yourself,
or, simpler for everybody, leave.

Here alone and centre-stage,
I'm hearing myself think.
I could get used to this. The children
are asleep and it's as cosy as the grave.
In fact, it's just the break I need:
strong female lead, harsh lighting
to show pain and courage, and sweet
as breast-milk, the audience attention.

The tendon in my neck begins to flicker.
I fix my eyes upon the footlights.
That rustling in the wings:

the other Hamlets are waiting.

2. Lear's Only Daughter

You come visiting, Dad,
with one small suitcase
and without your riotous knights.
All ghosts now, your drinking-pals,
summoned up for stories in the grim bar
where you eke out your days.
Dead, you say, cocking your glass,
from too much abstention.

You see me, don't you, as your good girl
who sat your shift and mine
beside my mother's hospice bed;
who held your cold hand
the night that thieves broke in
and carried off two coffee mugs,
a radio and your anniversary cassette.
But my voice was never gentle, soft
and low, and you won't wear
your deaf-aid, will you,
to hear my stern complaints
about the way her hard- earned pension
is disappearing on Australian white.

Dad, liven up. Get back
to the fine fettle of a rage,
throw my maths homework
at me again and call me thick.
Don't tell me now you love me.
I can see where it's all leading.
Dad, this fifth act's no place for us.

Her Sense of Line

By Joan Hewitt

Over my lover's head
on the wall of his bedroom
I see my daughter's present to him,
her painting of the fishquay.

She mounted it herself
without the right equipment,
and under the polished glass
the creases show.

In the hushed comfort,
next to brighter, well-framed
images, its blues and greys
are cool as water.

The line never wavers.
Delicate and sure,
it reels me in across the sea
to her and home.

Breath

By Maureen Almond

Somewhere, someone you know,
is busy dying,
and it might be an uncle
who was fantastic at the foxtrot.

He could be busy dying in Durham
while you count chimney pots
against a Penny Lane sky,
remembering the little things -

the coal that brought him here;
the black bullets in the chest,
the taste of them in your mouth.

You could be counting chimney pots
in the city where his father docked
with nothing to hand on, but rhythm.

There wouldn't be a sound in Langley Park,
because he'd be dying light on his feet,
to a little beat you've just remembered
when he whisked you round the floor of the *Pineapple*
and you were so proud of your uncle who could dance.

And the time and the distance between you
is lighter than a foxtrot,
no bigger than a chimney pot.

And the difference between dying and not dying
is so small,
it catches your breath.

Rhesus B Positive

By Maureen Almond

There's bad blood between us.
Tiny spots that are the proof of you,
nearly the death of you,
a hint that you might go the same way
as your two brothers, or two sisters
or your brother and sister.

I keep as still as a stranger,
talk to you only at night
and then in secret,
under the duvet
so that not even moonlight
can disturb you.

When the vibration of my whispers
threatens to shake you,
I take to avoiding words altogether,
bank up pillows to cushion my breathing
as it throbs like the night train
between brown bedroom curtains.

I picture the whole inch of you
wrapped up for your long journey
to my breastbone;
and so that you'll know it's me
you're fighting to hang onto,
I want you to picture it too.

Imagine your perfect fit
in the curve of my hip,
while I wait and listen for your eyebrows.

The Haircut as a Souvenir

By WN Herbert

I'm in one of the fifties astronaut chairs
in the Brooklyn Barbering Co. in Nelson Street,
squashed down so my hair can achieve terminal velocity,
and as the Robbie the Robot clipper-claw approaches,
I hear myself say, 'I know when it's too long
and I know when it's too short, it's the bit
in between that confuses me.'

I'm remembering the Hispanic shop
in downtown Manhattan, a cut for
50c that turns into a wash
a trim a shave a buff and a scare
from six of the hardest-looking barbers who
throw me back on the half-demolished street
with my skull and my prejudice shaved close.

Then there was the barber in Corfu Town
who filled his brandy glass again, and lit a fag, again,
and when you sat down he inhaled,
and when you stood up he drained the Metaxa,
all day – and in between, apart
from the ash in your ear,
you had been perfectly shorn.

And the haircut I had to have in Kolkatta
where men squatted, being shaved in the gutters
without a drop of blood rising
to join the clammy thunderclouds -
instead I entered a curtained caravan
where a cut and a head massage often leads
to something almost as intimate.

And by now the severed hairs prickle my neck
like the corpses of hundreds and thousands,
and the woman who cut me appears
to be describing the hair-dye of Arnold Schwarzenegger:
'It was orange, like wet cotton wool, and his neck
had blisters that should have been in his trainers,
and I said What did you use, and he said Flash.'

Play
(for Roo)

By Bob Beagrie

Through the lens of my daughter's microscope
All I can see is the ocean of my eyeball
Reflected back with a dusty archipelago
bouncing on the iris with every blink and jerk

What can ye see? what can ye see?, she bounces
Nothing, I say, spying the coast of Finland
With fishing boats navigating the sounds, I turn the focus dial
Until suddenly our coffee splat looks like a giant coffee splat

Before it's a lakebed of mud flats in the height of summer
One that definitely holds the shapes of woolly mammoths
Sabertooths...the odd plesiosaur or two

The leaf of basil, next, at just 3,000 times its size
Becomes a galaxy through a telescope, with stars, black holes and
nebulae
A petal from a geranium is a dead ringer for a solar system
Clinging to the nightshirt of a senile giant

A fragment of shell, as we guessed, was nothing more
Than the mountainous surface of the moon, but a pink feather
From her dressy-up bower, is the spit of glass splinters
Or patterns of frost in January

A hair plucked from her crown is a water slide at Lightwater Valley
While mine, with the root on, is a kwandao poised for battle

We try paper, a dead spider and some of its web
Then stick a chair (upside down) under the lens, and Alakazam
It's a cathedral. My clapped out car remains a rust-spot ruin
But our street is a vein in the throat of a shrew

The town is a blackhead in the crow's foot of the Cleveland Hills
The river's a tear trail from staring wide-eyed through the lens

Ritual

By Bob Beagrie

Old Blakey looks like he's lived in Heretu forever
As he squats on Fish Sands at the foot of the steps
In bicycle clips and Lieutenant Columbo's mac
His iron aged bike leans against the south sea wall

He takes out a powder blue dustpan and brush
Sets to dusting the beach into a Lidl carrier bag
Leaves a neat two-foot square of flattened beige
With bristled plough-lines like a garden in Kyoto

Climbs up the steps with his bag quarter full
Mounts the bike and peddles past the Pot House
To sit at home and sift for the tide's favourite grain
The beautiful one, the one with the World in

This is not Virgin or HMV

By Bob Beagrie

'I am interested in something which, by its very nature, is invisible'
Eva Grubinger, on her exhibition 'Dark Matter'

I could be Alice, Tom Thumb or Jack the Giant Killer
As I fidget in the ring made by Eva Grubinger's headphones
That I'll never grow to fit. They lie discarded, as if by an iconic bed.
There's a pending threat of presence in the absence of the giant.
No trace of Drum & Base, Dub or R & B, but I'm washed in stereo
By a thousand voices, distilled as the full-bodied liquor of dark matter.
A communal howl of static spirals thru the space between my ears
Like an old idea; except I'll never reach the mic to add my own whine
Even if I jumped. Its an archway, a bridge, a gibbet, and anyway
There's a sign that says, *Do Not Touch The Exhibits*.
I'm rendered solely as a listener to the sound of black paranoia.
One circle facing another. Each a mouth saying *Ooh! Ooh! Oh!*
As if trying to recall a vagrant phrase, or form a new
Word for surveillance on the tip on my lower lip.

The Girl that Lived in a Shoe

By Bob Beagrie

Small is beautiful.
Small   is   Beautiful
         Small equals petite
Petite is desirable.

Because the billboards proclaim it
It's a mantra pronounced daily
On prime-time, at breakfast
Calling all the faithful to worship.

So, I have decided to grow petite
And therefore beautiful, and refuse to eat
Finding ingenious ways to dispose of food
Resisting the urge to contaminate
My hollowness and my holiness

In secret
I am still fatter than a photograph
Of a girl on Redcar beach
Wearing a wide brimmed sunhat, a wider grin
And a child's forgivable pot-belly.

But I'm sure that I'm shrinking
little by little.
Soon, I'll be flatter
than the shadow on my bedroom wall.

As thin as the frayed string of white cotton
Running through the eye of a needle
And more desirable than my identical twin
Who always caught the first glance
From passing boys, men, and Dad.

These days I can slip through space, time
Even solid matter, on a calorific cushion of hunger
A thread of visions

In divine control of skin and bone.
Choice and will – my hammer and bell
Bind me tight as a foot in a Lotus Shoe.

I feed on air and light and luminous shades
That gather and dissipate, growing ever
More beautiful than starlight on wet branches
And their slim leafless twigs

More ethereal than antennae on a butterfly's head
More petite than a strand of cobweb swaying
From a kitchen rafter in Autumn draughts.

And those nurses shake their heads
Bring me medication and fattening drinks.
They fill my Shoe of Life with sighs
And I smile thinly, while my body tires

Of holding long-pig and cannibal in the same hand
Lacking the iron to pull the saturated moon to ground
I float like a seed, blown from a puffball wish
Counting, one o'clock, two o'clock, three o'clock
He loves me
He loves me not.

Rural Mischief

Two stories commissioned on the theme of 'rural mischief'.

The Warlick
(Warlick, pronounced 'waa-lick'. Cumbrian dialect. Rascal, devil, prankster)

By John Murray

Who was Jakie? What did he get up to, and why did he get up to it?
Was it perhaps a case of:

1. Harmless Lies?
Well, according to who he was addressing, he was a Pedigree Jersey
smallholder at Roadhead, capital of the remote North East Cumbrian
wilderness just below the Scottish border. He was also a New Orleans
sailor called Bub; he was a Norwegian mariner called Knut; he was
Hamish McGuffie, the best bagpiper and pibroch player from
Stenhousemuir, now settled in Copshaw Holm on the Scots side. His
adopted accents were scattergun imperfect, most of them learned
from Technicolor fifties movies watched in the old Brampton picture-
house. Once when drunk and addressing a deaf old lady visiting
Longtown from the Kielder Valley, this Norwegian sailor spoonerised
his name Knut to you know what, and it was remarkable how that
obscenity penetrated the old body's stone deafness. She struck Jakie
viciously on the ear and said she wanted no more dealings with a
foul-mouthed darkie-dago (her all-purpose designation for anyone
not Northumbrian nor Cumbrian and not snow white)...

We could go on forever about Jakie's mendacity, but we will be
selective. Suffice to say that he once told four Dutch tourists in the
Crossings pub, Roweltown, that there were still wild cats galore on
top of nearby Christianbury Crag, just as there had been when Daniel
Defoe visited Bewcastle and Roadhead back in the 1720s. Those poor
gullible buggers from Amsterdam shot off at once and took the hard
route to Christianbury up through that hellish impenetrable forest
past Cuddy's Hall and they are probably still there looking for
two-hundred-and-fifty-year-old wild cats nearly forty years later.

Jakie's actual marital status was single bachelor when he was
twenty-one in 1961, but he was always inventing himself wives of a
glamorous character and provenance. Especially, that is, when talking
to the very old, the very credulous, and those he was never likely to
meet again. His genuine occupations were part-time farmer and

part-time van driver, but it was the courier deliveries to new areas and new customers that really stoked his imagination. Once he boasted about his magnificent champagne wedding reception in Carlisle's Crown and Mitre, and added that his beautiful bride, a foreigner, was travelling with him today to keep him company. No, no thanks, she wouldn't want to come inside this Bellingham farmhouse for a cup of tea. You see, his newlywed was an African lady from Togoland, and she didn't really like to get out of his van. This was because a) she was extremely shy when it came to talking to strangers, and b) her Togolese custom was to belch, and far worse, if she was really pleased by the hospitality, break wind by way of gratitude. Sometimes he would horrify a nervous old widow by saying that his young Togolose/Iranian/Nigerian/Javan wife had only one leg and that the other had been bitten off by a leopard or a crocodile. He used this amputation motif in another context and regularly claimed to be facing a very serious operation in Carlisle hospital. Sometimes it was one leg he was losing, sometimes a leg and an arm, but the next time he visited them here in his van he would be wearing two perfect prostheses so they would never know the difference.

As a relevant addendum, we should point out that Cumbria is the home of the Biggest Liar In the World Competition, which takes place every summer down in Santon Bridge near Wasdale. Most of the tale-spinning competitors are elderly Cumbrian farmers but, curiously enough, Jakie Birkett of Pantingstown Farm, Roadhead, has never been known to be one of them.

2. *Elaborate but Harmless Hoaxes?*
Once, in 1962, fifteen women at a hen party in a Gretna motel stood with agonisingly bursting bladders for twenty minutes outside the locked ladies' toilet. Bafflingly, the one within who was hogging the bog, remained stonily impervious to their shouts and insults about her laying an egg or dying for her country. In fact it was not a lavatory at all, it was the bona fide room of a customer who was out for the night. Jakie, who had been jilted by one of the more unattractive of the hen party hens, had sneaked in the unguarded motel and had unscrewed the plastic letters L-A-D-I-E-S from their proper place and repositioned them elsewhere. It took him a good thirty minutes to do all this and he had had to employ an old and myopic look-out called

John Willy Crust (not his real surname). Such an imaginative, elaborate, incredibly painstaking trick is a long way away from the bag of flour or the drawing pin on the chair or the glue in the keyhole, and is certainly not to be laughed at.

3. Crude and/or Cruel Hoaxes?

Think of all the brutal hoaxes and deceptions in Shakespeare. Or think of Smollett's hero Peregrine Pickle, and the awful tricks he played on the ones who annoyed him. Now jump forward two hundred years to a pub half-buried in the forest up by Baileyhead. It is 1965 and Jakie is there drinking after hours with three or four of his cronies. He has just won a hundred quid on a bent hound trail race run on the Scots side, one which involved a twenty-year-old deviant called Slammer enticing the favourite Lusty Nell into a lonely sheep pen with a meat and potato pie. Jakie paid 1/3d for the pie and gave Slammer thirty bob for his part in the sabotage. The owner of Lusty Nell who had been released from her sheepfold after an extended lunch break, is called Tucker White. Tucker is drinking here at Baileyhead as well, and he is in a foul mood. He is aware of an act of crude sabotage, but he has so many enemies there is no one to point a confident finger at. Still, it is his habit to mock the nearest person when he is drunk and especially if they are as drunk as he is. So by five in the afternoon he is routinely referring to Jakie as Bucket rather than Birkett and he is taunting him with his exotic African wives of yore. As it happens, by 1965 Jakie is well and truly married with a two-year-old son and doesn't take kindly to this chaffing about belching grass-skirt darkies, as Tucker blithely calls them.

Suddenly, at twenty-past five, Slammer starts distracting Tucker with a hush-hush confab about next week's favourite at the Dockray trail near Wigton. Now observe Jakie Birkett slyly lifting out from his jacket a handy half bottle of Co-op vodka and tipping it into the remains of Tucker's fourteenth pint of the afternoon. The publican Alfie has already left these day-long boozers to it, and driven off to the betting shop at Longtown. There are Jakie, Slammer and two middle-aged warlicks called Sid and Sniffer left to witness Tucker downing that last lethal pint and then five minutes later sliding helplessly onto the dusty bar floor.

No sooner said than done. In a trice the four of them strip Tucker White naked as the day he was born. Slammer then hunts in the pub kitchen and finds a huge tub of cheap and sticky catering margarine used for spreading baps on darts night. The four of them rub the economy marge over every inch of Tucker's person, including his eyelids, elbows, kneecaps, backside, eyelashes, genitals, scrotum, hair, plus inside as well as outside his hairy earholes. Meanwhile Jakie has torn up a sheet of darts score paper into half a dozen pieces. On these he writes some odd little numbers. He presses these scraps of papers on Tucker's marge-smeared nose (20), tits (25 each), belly (50), left bollock (100), right bollock (100). They prop big Tucker up on a swivel bar stool and with Slammer holding him to stop him falling they spin him round once or twice so that the cleft at the top of his backside (150) is made visible, and then targeted. They then play a kind of adhesive hoopla-cum-coconut shy using an entire sweet-jar full to the brim with Alfie the publican's... pickled eggs.

The four competitors fling about fifty pickled eggs at bare-arse, bollick-naked Tucker, and their drunken dartsmanship is a treat to watch. Jakie wings both juddering bollicks with his eggs (200 points) and cheers triumphantly. Slammer flings a pickled egg between Tucker's buttock cheeks and it wedges there for the next half hour and the vinegar will ultimately weave its way into Tucker White's most sensitive and intimate depths. Then when they have run out of eggs, they gleefully pile into Slammer's car, drive off waggling down the hill to Longtown, and leave the mess and the naked mannikin with a pickled egg stuck up its bum... to its own devices.

Half an hour later, Alfie's wife returns from a Roweltown rummage sale and when she sees the naked, alcohol-and-vinegar-pickled spectre snoring and muttering on her pub floor, sure enough she screams in terror.

4. Bigger Warlicks than Jakie?
That all happened in 1965 when I was two years old. It is now the summer of 2001 and my father Jakie Birkett has just turned sixty-one. North East Cumbria's best-known warlick ought by now to be in his warlick prime, but as of the last six months Jakie Birkett no longer gets up to his tricks, neither big ones nor small ones, neither harmless nor outrageously crude. Slammer, his apprentice trickster, emigrated

to Canada in 1975, but even if he hadn't my father would have no zest
these days for teaching him how to give his enemies a heart attack. As
he puts it, if he bothers to put it at all, there is no point in telling daft
lies and playing daft tricks or concocting elaborate hoaxes when
doing it on a small scale has been superceded by other folk doing it
on an industrial scale.

What on earth does he mean?

Let's look at the word itself. Warlick is obviously a corruption of
the word 'warlock', meaning a male scourge or demon. An addiction
to pranks is sometimes described as an addiction to devilment, and as
he looks about him at deserted, bomb-blasted Pantingstown Farm,
and all the empty fields and empty farms nearby, my father is clearly
struggling to understand it all as the hoax or prank of some hideous
Super-Warlick. He doesn't blame his God above of course, not least
because like all North Cumbrian farmers he is loyal to his nearest
chapel. He certainly blames something though, Some Thing that he
cannot see or put a name to, and that is wilful, wayward and, above
all, pitiless. The something, the horrible thing, that is busy doing all
this malign and pitiless sleight-of-hand, is devoted to sham magic,
fake trickery and the most crude and brainless charlatan's brand of
hey presto.

Hey presto, cries the Super-Warlick! Look, out of nowhere, and out
of nothing, a magic hill of sleeping sheep, a flawless, immaculately
tidy pyramid of snoozing sheep. Where the hell did that come from,
gasps terrified Jakie, what sort of bloody warlick is up to what sort of
stupid game? They are all deep in an eternal sleep, Jakie, sigh the
rustling trees and hedges, they aren't baaing or chewing, much less
moving. Hey presto, once again. Look, one, two, three, at least a
dozen mile-long trenches. Abracadabra, now look again. The fields
all about, and for a radius of at least fifty miles, are all stripped bare,
as empty as the arctic or the surface of the moon. Not a single sheep
or lamb, cow or calf, goat or kid. Instead there is a lush pastoral
absence, a resplendent void free of anything but trees and plants and
birds and loudly humming insects...

Hey presto. A convoy of gigantic bloody lorries screaming and
roaring up these narrow North Cumbrian lanes. Lanes so obscure and
remote they normally see one three-wheeler and one Mazda pick-up a
day if they're lucky. Abracadabra. Now look at all these vast bloody

mats strewn across the principal highways, the A6071 for example. You stop at the mat, then drive slowly across it, and everyone, even the sheepdog in the back of the truck who hasn't worked for the past six months, knows that this mat-riding, this magic carpet ride, is all for fairy-story morale building, is as much use as sucking your thumb, and does nothing to halt the whatsit... the progress of the magic plague?

Then, worst hoax of all, there is the taking out. One of the Super-Warlick's favourite words is a really bloody queer one. It is 'contiguous'. One falls, and so they all have to fall. Spare no one, spare nothing, don't even spare the children, Jakie. All thirty Pedigree Jerseys in Jakie's case, tiny calves included, all of them with names dreamt up by my mother, all of them his glorified babyfied pets. There was only one vet sent up to Pantingstown that day, and she was only five feet tall so my father had to help her to do what had to be done...

Best draw a veil over that one, Jakie. You need to be a magician to draw a veil over that one. You need of course to be a Super-Warlick, not an ordinary one. This is really how I think my father sees it.

Welcome to Sheepworld

By Neil Astley

You'll all be wondering what you're doing here. Not a moment ago you thought you knew who you were. You were human for a start. And because you had a physical form – and there was that force you never cogitated much before called *gravity* – you were sure at least of where you stood. But your mind was wandering, your thoughts were elsewhere. You were off with the fairies. Dreaming. Or you'd reached that final stage of release from three-dimensional spatial existence.

And now you're confused and confounded, babbling and burbling, bewildered and bedazzled.

Bewildered because you thought for one nanomoment that you were dead and conked, and yet here you all are, not where or how you expected to be, true – why should that surprise you? – but you are nevertheless quite transformed. Translocated, transmogrified, quintessentially quondammed. You're not feeling your old selves.

And you're clearly *bedazzled* by our looming presence. That and the inescapable fact that we are a sheep. A sheep so massive in your former spatial terms that you are like ants beside us. We are a woolly behemoth towering over all of you, as loftily as fluffy white clouds in an azure firmament. If you could see the top of our head from high in excelsis it would be like looking down on banks of fleecy cumulus from a boeing jumbo. And those brownish specks you can just make out far below through gaps in the cloud cover, that's you, some city of your making. Either that or our gloriously splattered excrement.

We are the Ovine One. We loom but do not boom. Each one of you can hear our words as clearly and as softly as if we were sitting beside you, or as if you were silently reading them in a book, for that has always been the Way of the Sheep. Sheep do not need sound to commune with one another. Sheep have no need for elaborate noise patterning – what you call language – because sheep have unbabeled mindpower.

You hoodlum beings have evolved thousands of different languages and yet most of you can only parley one such tongue, another of the many ways in which you needlessly discombobulate, whereas all sheep not only understand each other but live and think in unison. You've seen the way hundreds of sheep will almost flow around a field when menaced by a hound. Your dancers need *years* of training to move together like a flock of sheep or birds. Had you not tried to distance yourselves from the other animals, you too could have evolved mindpower that might have matched that of cats or horses even if it could never of course equal the megamental energy of a sheep.

You thought God or Allah or some other mumbo jumbler had created you in their image, but of course *you* created *them*, and then – rather *ridiculously* you must now agree – you abased yourselves to serve their non-existent wishes, even killing each other for your makebeliefs and burblage, instead of getting on with your human being theres. And now you discover that the Creator – if we may use such a misleading term – has always been a *sheep*, and indeed the diminutive animal versions of us you know by that name were created in *our* image, not to rule your world OK – it was never our gameplan that *any* creature should bully over others, another one of *your* corkscrewed-up self-service hatchplots – but to enjoy the physical, sensory experience of humdinging wallowlife in the place we call Grassworld, the next but one parallel world to ours which you hairless apes for some reason have chosen to call the Earth. But since you're only familiar with *three* of its dimensions – your attempts to comprehend others, such as time (which was never the fourth), being somewhat tellytubbable – the Earth is perhaps an appropriate name for you earthbound clodhoppers to use.

Now being groundgrabbing grimlygits, you *do* like your explanations. You'll be pleased to learn then that on this momentabulous occasion – actually one of millions of such rapid transits in your lives – we shan't disappoint you. As mere homo-sapheads you will of course remember nothing of this afterwards in rational terms, human knowledge being so porridgey compared with that of sheep, but nevertheless it would be our hope that you will retain some residue of moral lightbulb, and thereafter you might at least show more kindlyness to other animals – to sheep especially – and not maltreat or eat them, nor molest them except when the wellington boot is on the other foot and the beast can pox you back, disease you in return.

That is an almost lastlegs task, a knackered hope we're well aware, given how little you've pubesced your respect for animals since your troglodyte ogtime, and forsooth how much you've latterly regressed, monking yourselves from the rest of the animal sheepdom in brick and concrete manpens.

You don't even work with horses now, so how can you be expected to know *anything*? It's no wonder you've become so obsessed with culling one another.

You need the presence of animals. You may not *think* they are using their superior mindpower to condescend with you, but talk to any saps who hang around with animals, not just to chuck tuck at them, but folk who live or work with beasts and birds, horse-riders, stable lads, snake-tuners, Inuits with their huskies, Chinese fishers with their cormorants, even so-called 'owners' of cats and dogs: they know their beasts aren't dumb.

Given the mindpower of such animals, they would verily be wally dumbos if they tried to mimic the esperanto of human discourse using vocal chords not suited to parroting your chitchat. Animals moreover have no probs in brainwaving each other, and they know what you're thinking even when you don't know their minds from mutton, so you shouldn't expect sheep to have any sharp incline to use soundwaves in interacting with jumped-up hindleggers when their grey matter has more megabytes of ram than your abacuses could handle in a month of Monday mornings.

The sheep's *baas* are merely functional, an ur-language for physical interaction between ovines, for calling lambs, warning of dog danger, tractor attack or bod on a quad; or voicing simple delight at the arrival of food. A sheep's field patter is mere bletherbawl and pasture roughstuff, like your street-talk, your ladloose grunts and catcalls, your crowd yawps and thumploud party lingo. A sheep's tonguefun and throatwarbling are no more speech than girlie shrieks and yobbish brayhaviour, the tuts and clucks of your chicken-in-a-basketcases.

But this is meant to be your moment of revelation, when all becomes clear as dayglo, so you don't really want to hear about animal blabbery. What *you* want is that neat tying up of loose and dangly ends after the climax of the film, when the smartalec calls a powwow in the drawing-room to crow you how he solved the mystery of. Even more you want that James Bond moment when the tuxegoed charmer is faced with final kaputting, but instead of bcing

82

deathblown there and then, he's subjected to Blowfly's boastful account of all his dastardly deeds and technowizardry. But then the hero makes his sudden sideways snakey move. Instead of 007 being fed to the Nazi sharks or sliced in two by the whining abbatoir saw, it's his wild-eyed adversary who meets that sticky, slicey mincemeat comeuppance.

Being human bozos, you are all hoping that the Almighty Bellwether will prove fallible in like fashion, and having lorded it over you – as you see it – this ovine colossus will puff up its gigantic woolly being and topple over, burst its lamb chops due to unforeseen circumstance or intervention, to plumdrop like Lucifer or Mrs Coulter into a bottomless shitpit, leaving you lot to return to your former earthbound lives.

We are genuinely sorry to disappoint you. And you needn't shuffle uneasily. Don't look dumblonde as if butter wouldn't melt in your buttocks. You forget that sheep have mindpower, and this Übersheep's immeasurable mental mainframe is what keeps this whole ramshackle show on the road. You forget too that sheep are incapable of overweening pride or presumption. We're all content in our sheepness, regardless of the physical pain, indignity and deaths you hoodlums inflict on our species in Grassworld.

Being human dunderheads, you cannot be expected to know that animals are higher beings, and that the sheep you simian mutants breed to kill and eat are the true Chosen Ones, the Woolly God's own creatures, for all sheep are Our Sheep. If they seem docile when you send them to their deaths, you should not mistake that for acceptance of the wrong you do them. They know that many must meet early painful passovers, but against that they balance all the time they're able to spend in mindful communion grazing in Grassworld. They also know that when the human rat-race finally selfdestructs, through global disease, nuclear soufflé or environmental casserole – and it's a toss up at the moment as to which of those will happen first – Grassworld will revive itself, and rid of man's harmful interference, sheep and the other animals will once again inhabit a balanced parallel world to this one. It is only a matter of time and sheeptime is on our side.

The end of the world is not the end of the match by any means, it is simply the point when you do-badders have committed so many fouls that the almighty ref – this very Sheep – finally gives you hooligannets the red card. Many species believe that you've been indulged for far too long already and should have been sent off centuries ago, certainly when you really started playing dirty during your so-called quote Industrial Revolution. After all your ransacking and habitacking, the banjaxing of the rainforests and ozone layer should have been the last strawberry, and handily our current projectiles show that this may well be the case, such are the environmental ramifications of those unbelievably drongo acts of global skinhead-ism. And you didn't even realise at first that forests and atmosphere might be interdependent, or so you dumdums claim. You must have thought photosynthesis meant using light to get nylon from trees.

Also: sacrificial lambs. A warning here for those whose belief-stretching systems hold that sacrificing a live lamb or sheep will please the Deity. Big mistake. Even the most shitbrained of you should realise now that holy jovicide will always be counterproductive.

End of lecture and general lambasting. We had to get that bit in while you're still eagerly waiting for your villain-reveals-all. If we couldn't give you a good sheep-ticking off each time you come before us, there would be no fun at all in this malarkey. Sheep have their own irrepressible sense of humour, as you'll know if you've ever eyeballed boisterous tups kicking, butting and guying one other as rutting-time approacheth, or seen field-gangs of lambs frolicking rambunctiously round the hedgerows. The older ewes might *appear* placid but while they're tearing at the tussocks they're all exchanging endless mindjokes; as their teats are being tugged by milkmad lambkins they pass those anchorage hours relaying fantastical shaggy sheep tales to one another, each yow elaborating a running mindjoke with her own inimitably droll embroidery. All sheep are fond of jokes and the Leader of the Flock is no exception, but if we have some custard pie at your expense, this is not so much to relish your ramboozled reactions to sheep japes and muttonry as to make our revelations easier for you to comprehend.

Sheep humour won't put you at your ease but it will at least send you off chastened and cheesed if only for two shakes of a lamb's tail.

So let's start with wool, since that's clearly been a source of itchycoo for some of you. Wool is the primetime element in

Sheepworld. Wool as in woolly, as in wholly or holy, for woolly means holy. That should have given someone a clue.

While you are our guests you will be woollier than those mammoths your club-wielding ancestors wiped out. Hence your appearance when you try to escape across the Parallel, for what those folk you're grasping to reach back in Grassworld actually see isn't white ectoplasm but your ghostly white wool. Ghosts have always been woolly and our darned wool will always pull you back into Sheepworld, such is its reversed magical mushroomism. You'll only leave here when you stop haunting the living, but first you have to be knitted out with a whole new identity.

Secondly, how you got here. Some of you *are* only dreaming, for when humans and animals dream they pass into our parallel world. The other animals benefit from Sheepworld's mindstretching recreational facilities, waking refreshed from their dream visits, their mindpower recharged by the wholly woolworth's experience. Dreaming humans, however – after counting sheep to get here – join their displaced brethren in a Dark Night of the Wool, along with the drug-crazed, the temporarily distracted and the recent dead, and when they surface from sleep some may remember a colossal tongue-lashing sheep but most retain only wisps of their mental mauling from the woolly juggernaut.

Readers are also drawn into our world, and when they look up on reaching the end they're left the mindprint that they only rambled ramwards in their imagination, and that the Allwoolly One laying down the sheeplaw was just some far-fetched farm fiction.

But the recent dead are another matter, quite literally for they have no matter now, they are spirit clothed only in wool, their spent flesh and bones now shucked behind.

Most of you here are ghosts, pesky souls on the loose, mentally agitated vagrants, displaced spirits without a body to call your own. And the fact that Sheepworld is only one of many parallel worlds you didn't know existed will only add to your confusion, nay your concomitant consternation, yea even your concatenated conclamation. But none of that will help you here.

Annoyingly for sheep, and inconveniently for you humans, there is also one other tiny world between ours and yours called Flukeworld, and you pass through there by a fluke. Nothing else exists there but flukes. Unable to live as parasites on other creatures, the flukes live inside each other's guts, for Flukeworld is not only parallel to both our worlds but inside-out between them. You cop it by some fluke; you reach here by some fluke.

If you're three-cherries lucky, you will go back to your world by some fluke event, the fertilisation of your next mother's egg by one miniscule opportunist sperm whooshed in that spark of life that sends your spirit looping back to Grassworld. If you're *very* cherry lucky, you may become your own grandchild or great-grandchild, but just as in politics, you don't have any choice; usually your past conduct will affect the outcome.

That's right, those shifty types over there have good reason to flinch, yes *you*: the erstwhile wife-beaters and cheaters, the warmongers and killers, exploiters and manipulators: it's all down to chance now but low-life attracts low-life and the chances are your next lives will *not* be so dandy, you may even be spending some time in the insect world; or swinging between maggot and mollusc, a whole succession of very short, decidedly unpleasant existences, whether as slugs, worms or dung-beetles. So you'd better get used to waving those antennae before some bigger bugger starts munching your chitin. It all depends upon just how nasty you were last time round. Murky pasts have a habit of catching up with you. Our big bad wolf in sheep's clothing will have you with extra fries. There's many a scuttling reptile that once strutted the streets in human form, thinking itself immune from attack, but no one escapes the Grim Sheeper when our giant ramrod hoof clobbers you from behind, smacks you across the back of your numbskull, whereupon in two shakes of said lamb's tail you find yourselves here.

If it weren't for Flukeworld, all sheep would enjoy more or less free passage between our two worlds, slipping into Grassworld for a spot of grazing then returning to Sheepworld for more ethereally sheepish pursuits. Some woolly chancers do manage these parallel world switches by working the odds on the flukes between. You'll all be aware that however many times you try to count the sheep in a field, it never comes to the same number. This is because they're always changing. The ones about to depart sit on their haunches, apparently bending over to lick or sniff their genitals, but when you look for them again, they've disappeared up their own arses,

the fluke's route out of the sheep and the sheep's way back
to Sheepworld.

And the shaman of course is half sheep, half man, hence their
name, and when they enter their trances they leave their bodies
behind to go on a daytrip to Sheepworld. That's a shaman over
there, that golden glow darting around like a snitch in a game
of Quidditch.

Your ancient Egyptians almost achieved shamanic wisdom.
They even worshipped a ram-headed god they called Ammon. Their
pyramids were scratching blocks for Ammon's hooves, for when he
had an itch in the frog. You'd have thought someone would have
guessed after that – Ram God, God the Son or Lamb of God, God
the Woolly Ghost – especially since in the Egyptian afterlife there
were human-headed ba-birds for holding souls until their release back
into the world, their version of what you've become, *baa*-birds, woolly
wispy temporary creatures of spirit, some of you trapped in lambo,
others about to fly back to new wombnests in Grassworld.

Eventually Grassworld turns into Sheepworld, for that is the frisky
nature of sheeptime. When you chumps finally cause the end of the
world as you know it – and you don't actually have much time left, so
try to enjoy your last incarnations – you merely wipe yourselves out,
which is something you've already done to so many other species it
shouldn't be that hard for you to imagine. However, you could never
actually destroy a planet which houses so many other interdependent
parallel worlds. All you will achieve, apart from your own demise, will
be the destruction of those parts of your world perceived by your
senses. (You only have five senses of course, whereas sheep have ten.)

Grassworld will then revert to its virgin state, these things being
cyclical, and your Earth will once again be covered with grassland
and forest, just as it used to be before you started encasing it with
concrete and bitumen like the Chernobyl sarcophagus. Too bad that
your little christingle orange blows out its own candle. This what
your future holds.

Your Saint Augustine said that the present does not exist because it
is instantly past. In Sheepworld we live in your future. Those of you
who are about to leave will shortly meet yourselves returning. Time is
cyclical like the seasons, and time in Sheepworld is both continuous
and eternally circular. In our beginning is our end. The moment you

depart is the moment you arrive. Everything you have just heard you are now hearing for the first time, so there was never actually anything to forget or remember.

We never get tired of saying this. Welcome to Sheepworld. You'll all be wondering what you're doing here. Not a moment ago you thought you knew who you were. You were human for a start...

Poetry for the Season

These poems were commissioned for a winter-themed event.

Gran's Diary

By Anna Woodford

All year December was coming
in your diary but you were
taking it one day
at a time: an arboretum walk
on 6 January; later that month it was
Herbert's funeral. On 8 February:
a talk on the crisis in music was
followed by the gas-man
after 12. All March,
though December was becoming
inevitable, you were making
other plans: putting lunch with Marge
before the nurse; seeing the doctor and 'The
Gondoliers'. It was 1999, people were talking
about the end of the world but you were
counting on another year: working out
the church cleaning rota into
the millennium; working out your savings
on three rainy days in April. A week's
holiday from 23 August was
ruled out by the consultant, then after a
hospital scan, it was the end
of Summer Time, the year's last quarter.
Your remaining days are mainly blanks:
the word 'mnemonic'
underlined; a book reference and
my name on 19 November with a question mark
beside it. A couple of weeks later
my name is ringed, red
lettered but this time
you didn't make it. Our arrangement then
is to meet again. You would have laughed
and said, 'Go on with you.' You were in heaven,

I was in December where, according to
your diary, death was no more
scary than a visit to the dentist
followed by the Clarendon Christmas Party.

Gran's Pantry

By Anna Woodford

After she died, everything in Gran's pantry
turned to leftovers. The calendar on the back of the door
stuck at November. The lightbulb popped,
unable to take the darkness in the room.
Her husband lived like a bird off the last of their food,
he thought he might die when he came to the end tin.
Nothing touched the grief gnawing at him
for the second time in his life. The first time
it was his mother who had gone.

Gran's pantry was the smallest part
of their house. It was a lady's portion.
It was a crumb brushed away
under the stairs. Its sealed jars were full of war,
they were up to their necks in dripping,
RSVP-ing, stiff upper-lipping.
They had been left standing
like the pillars of a toppled empire.

When she was alive, you could have eaten
your dinner off the pantry floor,
now it was covered in eggshells,
they cut his slippered feet
when he walked into the space
she had left behind her. It was huge.
This room was the preserve of his wife
and his mother.

After he died, following the will,
we raided Gran's pantry
and dug up the cake tin.
Inside was the hem of a coarse skirt
he had never let go of,
it was puffed up like pastry
– with diamonds.

They were the remains
of a fortune. The real jewels
had brought his mother back
from the camp a lifetime ago,
they had changed
in the guards' greased hands
to leftovers - a little bread,
a precious mouthful, some fruit.

La Donna

By Anna Woodford

The church is not broad enough
to accommodate your figure.
You put your faith in God anyway,
with a shrug of your covered shoulders,
with a wave of your fan. You kneel
before the statue of Our Lady and mutter
a prayer. Behind your back,
the flowers on your dress skim
over your body, they bloom
on your arse. A priest
should come running
to take up your fanning. An altar boy
should unfasten your Jesus sandals
and bathe each clay foot. You are older
than you look. You have come this far
after centuries. You have reached this point
with a prayer. I would praise you above
the hollow of your idol. I would raise you
above her shelf life of candles.

Summer Cold

By Anna Woodford

Today is so perfect, I am almost
living in the present, at the same time
I am noticing your face

has its history, separate
from mine, your forehead has nearly
been crossed out by lines,

you are coughing in spite
of the weather, you say it is just
a summer cold. I want to catch

the things you are saying,
I want to keep you
with me in the heat

of this moment as though
we could sit out winter
here in your garden, sipping

bitter lemon which will taste,
after today, like this time
with you, bottled. Our chairs are

temporary, they will fold at the
first sign of bad weather
and, already, a cold

is coming between you
and the sun and
the days that are coming

will get colder than
this one but I can
handle summer with you

under the harshest conditions.
Forget about winter.
Leave it to me.

The Tree

By Anna Woodford

When I raise my foot
off the ground, in line
with all the other women
and the couple of men,
I am expressing myself
simply as a woman
with a raised foot.
When I raise my hands
above my head, they are
swept up in a movement
of hands: of wrists and
of fingers. I hold
my position on an un-
equal footing in the yoga
group. At the far
corner of the room, shoes
cool their heels, our coats
are left hanging
while we turn - in our minds'
eyes - into trees. We are
posturing as a forest
together though December hard-
hits the window, our right
knees are unbending, our green
fingers are budding. The odd
rumble from a trunk, a
tumbling foot reveals
the beauty of this spot.
We are only human, it is
written all over our faces.
As a tree, I make a
good woman standing
on one leg. I know
what I must look like
and I'm happy with that.

The City in Winter

By Jacob Polley

We're sick of the cinema, its lobby buttered with light,
of riding home on Iron Age bikes,
bags of booze swinging from the handlebars,
our coats full of smoke and our hair rock-hard.
Sick of the rooms the street-lamps carve
out of the fog and the intimate dark.

Sick of parks put aside to be cold in
and pavements that glitter and ring;
of the ways winter sets off the city,
yellowing the pubs and the bakeries,
floating the hospital's fumigant globes
on the hill, evacuating roads,

twisting fibre-optic washing-lines
through backyards of icy brick. Now all windows shine
with a wealth of warmth, their curtains cracked with gold.
Cars, conceded to frost's lunar hold,
lie abandoned at bus-stops and crossroads
and we wait hopelessly for snow,

knowing it's somehow delayed by the sea,
which still works, despatching its white birds to wake us,
scraping on the wind. How long can we live
with the clock set back, at a loss,
our footsteps falling like pennies?
The city wants to melt us into its shops,

would draw us through blazing doorways,
past scent-counters and watchcases,
our souls drab and clothes grey,
the long mirrors licking our faces.
There's a great tree at the centre of town
we're sick of and our throats are wound

with inherited scarves. For we know winter
from the cot, with its bone-cold bars,
from the damson-dark nipples
of our mothers, whose fingers are whittled
under running water as we ride home,
each light opening a door in the stone.

Four Sea Views of Winter

By Peter Armstrong

June: The Émigré

There are the antipodes:
that pale sky continent
whose blue is white;
whose constellations burn
into the frost-occluded eye
their pinprick after-images
so absolute that night.

Time's ocean ushers you
along its steady currents
and the landmarks rise,
describe a shallow arc to port
and pass. No landfall, then:
only this adherence to the O;
only this so slow descent
down from the globe's low summit
towards its pure, receding edge.

September: The Surfer

Although the wave has undermined itself
(hollowing of shadow; gleam in the abyss),
my soul yearns down into that furrow
where everything or nothing is.

Only keep me hanging on this lip,
the glimpse of dark insisting,
as the blue burn of the sun
when the lid blinks shut, insists;

or hang me by this thread of spume
midway down that wall of death
(I say this straight out, as a dare)
so that the one who holds his breath

before the last disclosure comes
(the brink commencing its collapse)
might come to knowledge, and not care
(you seal, or pull apart your lips)

January: The Arctic Colourist

You'd thought that nothing must be black:
at least (or most) that pulse
beneath the flicker of the lid.
Now everything is razed to this:
the bleached void at your back;
ahead, the needle of the hail.
You pray for night,
but find yourself turned loose
upon this blinding ground.

A lash against the skin of the eye;
cold salt rubbed into the eye's raw wound

April: The Departing

A rising tide, the usual displays;
the headland flowers none of us can name.
The dying surgeon put it into words:
Leave resurrection to the resurrectionists
but he was wrong: another year of birds
is fouling the ground beneath their nests;
the band is playing Anchors Away;
someone waves a handkerchief. A shame.

Seven Versions of Winter
(After James K Baxter)

By Peter Armstrong

Winter by James K Baxter

Winter unbundles a sack of storms
Above the flat scrub country.

Far at sea a trawling captain
Watches a double rainbow arching,
Noah's good sign, along the black horizon,
Hopes for groper, fat cod, terakihi.

A beaurocrat lights the gas fire
That warms his raw-edged afternoon,
Plucks a folder from a grey steel file,
Coughs, and eyes the telephone.

A housewife sees her washing, three days' wet,
Hang draggled in the tugging wind,
Measures the old chair for new covers,
An ache of winter in the mind.

A child dawdling home from school
Builds little twig dams in the gutter,
Sings to himself although his shoes
Are damp, and bullies lurk at Butcher's Corner.

Winter unwraps a parcel of stones
For old and sick and sad, and homeless walkers.

1. The Form of the Poem

The weather acts its grudge out on the land.

Frozen on their continents
this occurs, then this, then this.
The instances enjoy, or must suffer
their occasions, as we observe
– or, rather, you, reader:
God at your impossible distance –

the abstract mind eroded
by the freeze and thaw of stuff:
the weather picking at the quarry face,
that bark, your skin

2. An Appropriate Myth

October, ramshackle goddess
fills the river with this dark frothing beer.

Each tributary burn
has laid the grasses flat
beneath its perfect
seal-back skin
and eaten one more morsel
from beneath the rootball of the ash.

A libation poured from sky to ground;
The dishevelled goddess blessing
the benighted in the fields, the drowned,
the hungry walkers and full crows
that everywhere do reverence.

3. Arc

The year, without a change of course
tips its face from the sun and shrugs.

Mothers in their sleep attend
to nuances of chill around the house,
the moon's slashed angle on the floor,
the breathing of each room, the hush.

Stranded in their pier-end reviews,
the kings of slapstick sigh to note
another empty row. In keeping with tradition
they roll their eyes and vanish into smoke.

The liturgy shifts gear. Accountants
smooth another ledger page and wait.
Great youths who came to nothing
admit what they cannot admit.

The year moves on its pivot
and the dusty mechanism gives a groan.
The cuckoo ends its shift
and hands the billet to a crow.

4. Alas! Literature Occurs

Snow falls.
Maloney gnaws his way through *Ulysses*,
his elbows rubbing out against the desk,
the chill that wraps his wrists and ankles
whispering of lives.
The bars are chocker, though;
the slush is packing into ice
between the cobbles of the quay;
and that sparrow (or that finch – how would he know?)
is doing something out of reverence to Bede
(or was it Colum Cille?) which brings to mind
the snow, drifting like cold scurf,
a cataract between the here and now

5. Grey at Falloden

Winter sends dispatches home:
news from the front, an arrow
on the map, another term.

Here, a dipper
scratches phrases in the Dene;
from the burnt paper
of Beech leaves, thin
imitative starling voices.

Winter wires disasters and remembrances:
the salient and city clenched,
a chalkbed stream, the dear departed.
Bereaved of song, the rutted ground is raising
something like a prayer for spring.

6. At Criccieth

A cold sea pulling shingle
round the scoop of the bay,

the local papers have abandoned
fictions thinly dressed against the elements
and announced their own demise
in banner headlines printed white.

A season combing back the ocean
and the grey sheen of the grass,
and the zen garden of the numbed brain
where the self walks ill at ease.

You tell yourself that this will pass,
which is a lie, or at best a fiction, or a tease.

7. Act V, Sc. II
Feste's song concluding...

The gates swing shut and the rain begins to fall.

Whether to the piss-pots and the barren marital bed
or to the rain-swept plazas of the night-abadonned capital,
he steps with a hey! and a give-away slope of the head
out of the lights and into the squall

An inner door is heard to close

                                  and the rain, with great tact
runs its tender fingers down the runnels of his cracked
noble face.
                  Applause.

It Started
With a Song

*For this event, the writers were invited to create new stories
and poem sequences inspired by a song of their choice.*

Listening to Madonna

By Angela Readman

I've yet to get the scarf, those red and white markings to keep me warm the day before Valentine's. Or the puffa jacket people will say is far too big for me, that gives me the opportunity to let everyone know I am loved. It's that easy. That visual evidence to put me up there with the real girls, the lasses with Puma coats and gold.

Jeanette walks past with her cronies. They wear an armour of fuck-off flick, Insette hard hats that don't let our gaze seep in. They clop down the hallway in order of size. Teetering Jeanette in cerise stilettos and ankle socks, Judith, then Elaine – the robotics girl; I'm still trying to decide if she's cross-eyed. Maybe a bit, but no one's going to say it while she knocks about with them.

They pass. A name in black marker on the side of Elaine's bag: *Denty,* with a heart beside it. It's a skinny excuse for a heart, skewwhiff, more like an arrow, way off target.

'What do you think?'

Lisa-Marie rolls her eyes, looks down at them through the glass doors. 'Which one?'

'All of them. Any.'

'Elaine's still a virgin. Judith's done the wankathon. Jeanette's bought the T-shirt.'

'Yeah, shame she's too busy fucking to wear it.'

Lisa-Marie laughs. Deep in her throat, it sits there, laughter like a sliced rind of bacon. Lisa-Marie can be trusted to know such things, like I can be trusted to listen. I never argue with her opinion, but sometimes scavenge for greasy off-cuts of knowledge.

'How d'you reckon?'

'Well, look at her.'

She raises her eyebrows like there is no more to say. I watch Jeanette's pins grow smaller down the corridor, the blonde flick on her brown hair turned away.

'Howay, just coz she looks slutty...'

'She's going out with her brother's mate. Last week she came in with a new ring.'

'How old's he?'

'18.'

'Ah.'

The sovereign rings have a lot to say, because they make you see the small cubic zirconia nestling on the finger next to it. Not the sort of thing you notice right away, but once you comment on the knuckleduster, that's next. The runt sister beside it, she tells you was a Chrissy gift off him. The ones with boyfriends their own age wear silver lockets someone like Sharon Emms says is sweet. Before she turns away to her mates and whispers loudly, 'Silver? I wouldn't piss on it.'

'Come on, let's test our form,' says Lisa-Marie. 'It's time you took the test. Hold out both hands. Not like that. I'm not reading your fortune, I'm reading your now.'

I turn my hands over, undercooked chipolata fingers.

'Relax your fingers, they're like dicks at a disco.'

I let my fingers go limp, outstretched but pliable when she touches them.

'Have you ever kissed anyone?' Lisa-Marie looks right at me, blue eyes that could reflect a lie.

'Yes.'

'With tongues, mind?'

'Yes.'

She turns one finger down at the knuckle and moves on to tug the next.

'Ever been felt up, above the waist?'

'Yes.'

'Corny?'

'What do you think?'

Corny was his name, but not really the word that sprang to mind when I think about our romance. I went round to his house every night for six weeks, watched him play Subbuteo till it was time to set me halfway home.

Lisa-Marie moved onto the next finger.

'Under the clothes?'

'Yeah.'

'Below the waist?'

'Yeah.'

'Below the waist under the clothes?'

'Licked out?'

I hated the words, an instant image of me as a kid asking to wipe the bowl clean of sticky sweet butterfly mix.

'Urgh. No.'

'Rubbed it over the clothes?'

'Sort of, more of an accident.'

'Done a blowjob?'

'No.'

'Have you ever had sex?'

'No.'

She smiles, does a quick count of which fingers are left standing.

'You are 50% virgin,' she pronounces.

'50?'

'Well, I'm not sure if the accidental jean-job counts or not.'

The bell rings, and we walk together till science lab.

'This is me. See you at the gate when we kick out.'

Madonna is singing, that's all... She stands on the steps, a monument with James Bond-like pigeons surrounding her, turning her face away from the flowers they offer, accepting bracelets. Boys can kiss, boys can hold, but they can't have her. Only she can see the light of a YTS Mr Right.

Lisa-Marie opens my make-up box, picks out the blue mascara and begins making elaborate swooping motions on her lashes. I'm dicking about with the curling brush, scrolling it round my fringe.

'Pass me the hairspray. Quick.'

She tosses the hairspray to the floor, where I'm in prayer in front of the mirror.

'Shit. I've lost it. It's never gonna go like hers.'

I look at the record cover: Sam Fox's perfect unachievable do.

'Course not. Hers is layered and it's longer.'

'What can *I* do then?'

Lisa-Marie looks at me, considering my options, given the limited resources.

'I'd settle for Cybill Shepherd,' she says.

Lisa-Marie knows more about hair than me, on account of her mam who knows everything there is to of home perms. Lisa-Marie is just lucky; so blonde there isn't a name for it. I look at her, knowing she will be one of those women who never have to dye.

'You got homework?'

'Maths.'

'You?'

'English.'

Lisa-Marie is some sort of maths whiz. She looks at the numbers and they stick. One time she'd tried to teach me, just try and think of them as amounts of things you're interested in. Percentages like the virgin test, fractions of innocence, boys with cars divided by the amount of girls in my class desperate for one. It never took. Now we swapped exercise books, and she breezed through the maths homework it would take me hours to complete, incorrectly, in fifteen minutes. The handwriting didn't matter; it wasn't too dissimilar. Every week or so I tried a different kind of handwriting anyway, trying on which one suited who I was. If you were to try to guess what I'm like by my latest handwriting I'd be a girl of a cheery disposition. Smiley faces above my *'i's*. Hearts where a full stop should be. Truth is it just made me easy to copy. Lisa and me could be one another just like that. In exchange for maths I did English – a bit more difficult on the handwriting front. I'd practise her wide *'a's* and leering *'e's*, the swinging loops and careless *'t's*. If Lisa-Marie and me merged into one person I reckon we'd be all right.

'If Alcatraz asks, you're on the side of pro-zoo.'

Alcatraz was the English teacher I had in first year, and Lisa-Marie had now. Her real name was Jones and she was the exact opposite of who we wanted to be. Brown leather shoes, A-line skirts, imprisoned fringe not a hair escaped from. Lisa was going to be something more glamorous: a personal assistant in a sheer white blouse with a view to an affair with her boss. I was less certain. Florist if I didn't pass GCSEs, something more hazy where I could only see a red car and a pinstripe suit if I did.

'Zoo? I fucking hate zoos.'

'Aye, but you'll get more marks if you mention preservation of endangered species and shit.'

'Cool.'

Lisa-Marie closes the maths book. 'Finito.'

'I'll have yours finished by the morning,' I say.

We stand by the fence near the farm, watching a horse let out a giant stream of piss.

'Look at that dirty bastard,' says Lisa-Marie.

She passes the cigarette to me, and I inspect it between my fingers.

'It's a fucking horse, what do you expect?'

'Look at the fuckin' size of it!'

The horse's bits hang between its legs. When you least expect it, a giant obscene lipstick suddenly appears on the not-quite smile of the Mona-Lisa. I take the cigarette to my lips and let the smoke dawdle in my mouth.

'You're not doing it right; you're supposed to inhale, like this.'

She takes the cigarette from me, and draws on it, end slightly soggy and lip glossed as she passes it back to my inexpert hand.

'Fuck this, the horse is putting me off.'

We turn away, head towards the park; over the road a lad in a bomber jacket is walking up the bank. Lisa looks at him, and keeps walking. Cigarette perched between her fuck-off fingers.

'I can't come out tomorrow tonight,' she says.

'Why not?'

It is the first night since the grounding we haven't been together. I wonder if there's someone living nearer who Lisa's hanging out with instead of me.

'Confirmation classes.'

'What is it, like religious?'

'Yeah. Me mam wants us to, or you can't get married in church.'

'Classes? What about?'

'They tell you about God and stuff.'

'Every week?'

The evenings of boredom stretch before me. No one to tell things to that make my thoughts seem like they really exist.

'Where they at?'

I hoped she'd say a church nearby, somewhere I could meet her after when she came out dipped in religion. I could walk her home, share a bottle of pop, be the first to initiate the post-church 'fuck' from her lips.

'Near my dad's.' She flicks ash off her coat, little white flecks on her donkey jacket, like a workman surprised at snow in summer.

That was that. Lisa-Marie is funny about her dad. Whenever she goes there she comes back with biscuits and pocket money she buys cheap crisps with. We eat them and make Cola slushies in the freezer, as she tells me about her dad's flat and his bus-driver bird. I see him through the windscreen when he drives off, tanned face and brown hair, like one half of my cousin's Starsky and Hutch, legless and plastic in a tiny aluminum Matchbox car.

'I didn't know you believed in God.'

'Dunno, but at the end you get a new dress and a cross and chain.'

Little girls in white wedding dresses and veils. That's all I know about religion, that and the Brownies thing in the juniors. My mother beamed proudly as I walked down the aisle in a bobble hat and leather belt, the rest of the Pixie pack following behind. I'd held the overripe orange carefully, with the candle in the middle, the juice oozing from the peel making my hands sticky as infected pores. The things on the cocktail sticks had something to do with God. The Father. The Son. The Holy Ghost. The Virgin Mary and miscellaneous guests. They poked out from the cellulite earth as the priest lit my candle and I took my place in line at the front of the church. As the organist began *Oh, Come, All Ye Faithful*, the waft of citrus hit me. In a second I popped a green midget gem baby Jesus into my mouth; it was good. Mouth watering. He tasted of lime.

I'd left the brownies shortly after I'd made sixer. Everything was going too slow. I looked at the badges on my tunic and wanted more, faster than brown owl would fly. Neat symbols to show who you are, in embroidered black triangles – *hostess, homemaker, camper* – and I wanted more. *Chef, armed combat, sex kitten.*

'Were you ever in the Brownies?'

'Hell no,' she laughs, 'I wouldn't be caught dead in a beret.'

It figures. Even at nine I imagined Lisa-Marie in court shoes, a candy cigarette dangling from her lips, the pink end she looked at and bit off first. Confirmation, another sort of badge, and a new dress, like an audition for getting married someday. Lisa-Marie would be ready. It had nothing whatsoever to do with me.

Today Madonna knows the angels. She knows someone must be an angel. I think about Devil in Disguise, and it is a long way from here. You are an angel, you must be, I can see your wings somewhere behind your mascaraed eyes.

In my bedroom we resume the test. We went to mine, to avoid her sisters who pissed the bed, popped their heads in and out the door, and giggled through the stairwells at overheard snippets of our conversation. Anyway, I had more singles. We lifted the arm back, let the same one play four or five times till we wanted a change.

I go to the turntable, put on another record.

'I never did the virgin test on you,' I says.

'Go.'

Lisa-Marie jumps on the bed, and I sit opposite. She tucks a cushion between her legs and spreads her hands out on each knee.

'Kiss?'

'Yip.'

'French?'

I wasn't sure what I thought of the term. It conjured up images of snails passed back and forth in a warm garlic sauce, and undercooked meat of uncertain origin I'd had on the daytrip with school. But I was trying how it felt on my lips anyway, fresh from the pages of *Lace*.

'Pleeese.'

'Felt up?'

'Yip.'

'Under clothes?'

'Yip.'

'Been poked?'

The expression reminded me of pink pigs, like the ones I'd seen at pets corner, loads of them wriggling and sucking at whatever they could get round beached mothers.

'Yip.'

'Under...'

'Yep.'

'Had a love bite?'

'Yep.'

'Give one?'

'Yep.'

'When?'

'The week I wore the snood.'

'Done a blowjob?'

'No.'

'Wank?'

'Yep.'

'Have you ever done it?'

'Yes.'

'Who?'

'His name's David. He lives in Southbank. You wouldn't know him,' she says.

'What was it like?'

'It was good,' she said. 'Fuck this shit. Are you gonna put some Wham on or what?'

Lisa-Marie traces her finger over the cover of *Bad Boys*.

'Mmm. That's my idea of the ideal man.'

'Give me The Pet Shop Boys,' I say, 'or Andy Bell.'

'You've got a lot to learn,' she says. 'Everyone you like is gay.'

My version was less graphic than Lisa's, so I suppose she was bound to come out best. I knew I should have done the Virgin Test on Lisa first, so I could give the same answers, nothing too gross, but nothing to leave me lagging too far behind.

They made me take off the studded belt and cross earring. Somewhere there's a poster of Madonna laughing, hair flopping in her eyes, burying her face in her hands.

I walk into the room and take a quick scan around. No teacher yet. Bubblegum cracking, lads sitting on desks, lasses etching their loved ones into the wood with a compass. You could hear the noise before you walked in. Fatty Mellard's never on time. I always sit near the wall at the back by myself. I edge down the aisle of bodies, invisible, about to sit down when he is there.

'What are you doing?'

Taylor is stood with a white grin right in front of me.

'What does it look like?'

He looks around, to his mates watching him from the window wall.

'What are you doing?' he repeats.

Tick-tock. Tick-tock. The second hand seems to be stuck on the same place.

'You know you're not allowed to be in the classroom with your coat on,' he says.

'So? The teacher isn't here yet. Who'll know?'

'I know.'

I'd snitch under torture. I scan the classroom for evidence of bodies in coats so I can point someone else out and save myself. There aren't any; girls in white blouses, or black jumpers with breasts propped on the desk.

'So?'

'I'll tell him, as soon as he comes in. With your coat on, you're not ready to learn.'

His mates howl in the background.

'Take it off,' he says.

'I'll take it off when he turns up. It's freezing in here.'

'No one else looks cold to me.'

I shrug and take another step towards my desk, when he steps in front of me.

I take a step to the side. He's already there.

'Take it off and I'll let you sit down.'

'What's it got to do with you?'

He grins.

'Off.'

He leans towards me, and places his hand near my throat, runs it down the lapel on my jacket to my top button and unfastens it. Slowly. Looking into my eyes, trying not to blink above my sizzling cheeks.

There were ways to handle situations like this. Breathe. Count to ten. Go for the bollocks. I try to imagine what Jeanette would do. She wouldn't be stuck in the corner like this, or maybe she wouldn't mind so much.

'Pack it in.' I bring my hand up to push him away. With one hand he catches it, unfastens the next button with the other.

A cheer through the lads' aisle.

'Yeahhhh. What you doing, man? Getting a feel of her tits?'

Taylor laughs, looks over his shoulder at them.

'Nahhh. I just wanna get a look at some.'

The door swings inwards, and Taylor looks towards it. I nudge my way to my desk and sit behind it, clasping my coat, going in my bag and taking out anything that buries my face.

Fatty is stood at the front in his bingo caller's jacket, a tyre tread of dust running up one sleeve from the time he was ran down on the lash.

'Desks, people.'

Taylor walks away, grinning, turns to look back at me as he goes.

'That means you, Taylor,' he yells.

He sits.

'Sir, sir,' he raises his hand, grinning, 'she's still got her coat on.'
Taylor thumbs in my direction, and the class turn to look. Fatty
frowns.

'Coat off, Miss Walker,' he calls. 'I've told you about this
before. Page 7, people, and after the first exercise bring books to
the front.'

I stare at the fractions on the white page, numbers with black
slashes between them like negative roads. I take my coat off and
push my chair back as far as it will go. Pen in my hand, face almost
touching the cool paper, I work on making numbers relate to each
other, as slowly as I can.

*Sometimes I don't know why we go outside, where there's no music. No dancing next
to a lion, or practicing pouting, or being beside her in a Gondola, as she sings us
through Venice.*

'You got a light?'

The lad in the bomber jacket stands beside us. I trail my feet
along the ground beneath the swing and slow down. He is talking to
Lisa-Marie.

'Yeah.'

She takes a box of matches from her pocket and strikes one along
the side. He cups his hand over around her flame and leans in.
I don't know him, but he looks familiar. He doesn't go to our school.
He is older, one green eye and one brown, like David Bowie. I
wonder how it happened, if he'd been born that way, or if a spark
had left a bonfire and flown into his eye to leave its amber there.

He looks at Lisa, and I pretend not to be watching him, eyes at the
dust my shoes make trailing on the path, and across to where they are
standing by the slide.

'I've seen you before. What's your name?'

'Lisa.'

'You live up the hill, right?'

'Yeah.'

117

'I've seen you walking home from school. You look like someone I used to know.'

I can see her smiling.

'You come here much?' he says, moving his arm to his lips, and puffing on the cigarette that seems like an extension of him. Sucking in, to make the end glow bright.

Give me a break, it's virtually a come here often. But Lisa doesn't pick up on this, or if she does she thinks better of back-chatting in her usual way.

'Sometimes,' she says, that's all.

'I'm Boothie. Probably see you around sometime then.'

'Yeah, you never know,' Lisa says.

He raises his hand without turning back, a sort of wave, as he walks away.

Madonna was crazy for someone. Never wanting someone as much as this.

'What was it like?' I said.

Lisa-Marie was tying a piece of lace under her hair. She took the ends and made a knot, fiddled in the mirror with a bow, and brought it to one side. She took eyeliner off my dresser and made a small dot above her lip.

'What does it look like?' she said.

'Minnie Mouse trying to cover a zit.'

I looked at my hands, naked of nail varnish, and back at Lisa-Marie.

'What was it like?'

'What was what like?'

'Doing it.'

She tugged at the lace without untying, left it as a parcel hurriedly unwrapped on the side.

'It was good.'

'Just good?'

'Unbelievable,' she said.

I thought of the women in their plunging necklines on her mother's novels. Scarlet O'Hara bent over backwards for a kiss.

'Did you...?'

I was struggling, raising my eyebrows, making a circular motion with my wrist like a tumble dryer.

'Did I...?'

Lisa-Marie mimicked the motion, her hand making clockwise of my anti-clockwise turns.

'You know... *come*.'

'What do you think?' she looked at me, rubbing off her faux mole with a pinky full of spit. 'Twice.'

'What was it like?'

'Good.'

I wanted more. Good like a new pair of Pods or good as sucking a hot cup of coffee through a Twirl? I'd tell her everything, like best friends are supposed to. But Lisa-Marie liked the sound of one hand clapping. Trees falling in the woods only made a sound, I reckoned, if your best friend was around to hear of it.

'You try it.' She threw me the lace. 'Put it in your hair.'

I unfastened the lace slowly, three of her pale hairs still clinging to it as I looped it round my neck.

'Soppy shite.' She lifted the record off and threw it on the carpet and replaced it with Frankie, a foot march of two tribes going to some kind of war.

I try to find and not let out of my sight the first star I see tonight, Madonna says she knows it'll make everything alright.

Boothie's mate stood beside him. There was something about him that made me faintly sick. Yellow streaks on brown monk-brushed hair. Gap between his front teeth that always made me think he was telling a lie.

'We're having a party on Saturday night,' he said. 'My mam and dad are going away for a dirty weekend.'

'Smart, who's coming?'

'Everyone, some of my brother's mates. Tell your mam you're staying at your mates so you can stay out late.'

He handed over a slip of paper with an address written on in letters that couldn't decide what they wanted to be. Some capitals, some small letters, the house number underlined unnecessarily.

'See you there,' said Lisa. She folded the slip of paper, and put it in her pocket.

I heard him whistle and spit on the ground as we walked away.

'Will you mind these for me?'

Lisa-Marie was wearing the black fitted jacket with blue leopard-print collar and cuffs; it seemed to make her hair even paler, like vanilla ice cream melting down her face. In her hands she held a three pack of johnnies. *For her pleasure*, the packet said, not for your pleasure. There was something illegal about them, the word latex burning into my palm as I took them from her.

'What for?'

'Our Paula keeps going through my stuff.'

Paula was an oddity – the youngest of Lisa's sisters, just about to come to our school. I liked her more than the others, but there was something about her that was lazy. The way she looked at you, and smiled a slow smile like she was beginning to understand something. She draped the sofa and armchairs at Lisa's, hanging from them, long thin legs dangling from a green satin slip that used to be her sister's, habitually licked lips giving the impression of lipstick.

'She found a johnny in our Julie's room, and blew it up.'

Strange Paula, who was too old to not know there was something illicit about Durex and too young to know exactly what. I imagined her blowing up the condom, putting a note inside, her small polished pink fingers balancing it through the window before she let it float into the clouds.

'Besides,' she said, 'the pockets in this thing hold fuck all.'

I put the box in my pocket, prodded it through the hole in my lining till I was free of its square edges on my thumb.

I looked at the sleeve, the boy-toy belt and waist-length bra.

Lisa-Marie left her bra on the floor by my bed once when she'd stayed. When she went to the loo I picked it up, tried to look at the size. A neat frayed strip sat in the underarm, a scissor line where *wash by hand* and other important info used to be.

'Do you like him?' I said.

'He's all right,' said Lisa. 'Not exactly George Michael.'

'He's got eyes like traffic lights, I never know which one to look at when he talks.'

'Yeah, he might be all right if it wasn't for that.'

'So you don't like him?'

'He's OK, I suppose.'

'Why are we going then?' I asked

'I dunno. Summat to do.'

I never knew what Lisa-Marie thought. I was sick of talking. I flipped the record off and flung Madonna on.

'Oh, I fucking hate her,' said Lisa, 'she's a fucking tart.'

'She's singing about being a virgin though!'

'No, she's singing about being *like* a virgin, it's a whole other ball game.'

'I suppose.'

I looked at the sepia Madonna and Madonna looked back. Madonna wore her underwear on the outside. Madonna had sex and you knew it. Lisa wasn't giving me fuck all.

Lisa-Marie's mam put down another paperback with a photo of a woman smiling on the front. It wasn't a cover like the others. Usually they were paintings in reds and golds of ladies with manes streaming behind them, arms round tiny waists. Curved backed they leant into military men, waiting for a kiss with their eyes shut. Men and women from the olden days, with only cleavage, like strawberries for sale, between them. The women had names like Raven and Sapphire, girls who fell in love with men who always knew better, and always came back for them in the end.

Lisa-Marie's mum turned to me as soon as she closed the book, and grinned.

'Hiya, chuck, she ain't in.'

Paula had answered the door and let me in. Now I wasn't sure what to do.

'You can wait if you like, she shouldn't be long. PAULA?' she yelled.

Paula slipped into the room.

'Go down the library and take these back, will you, cock?'

She slipped a pile of books across the carpet.

'Do you want anymore getting?'

Lisa's mam gave her a look. Paula sighed, slipped some shoes on and as she slammed the door Lisa's mam yelled after her, 'None of that Mills and Boon shite neither.'

'What's wrong with Mills and Boon?'

'Nowt, pet, but they're all the same. Just a bunch of virgins falling for older men.'

Perched on the edge of the couch I looked around the room for something to talk about.

'Photos? Can I have a look?'

It'd probably be a bunch of people I never knew, countless aunts and uncles, but at least I'd have ahhs and oows to say as she pointed them out.

Lisa-Marie's mam took the album out from under the sofa with both hands. It was red, leather effect with gold letters on the cover that said *Our Family* in curly script. She made a small motion from her top knuckles, emerald polish inviting me in as she opened the book. Inside was a glossy photograph of Elvis in a bolero jacket. The next was a black and white image; he stared at a record player on his knee, at the disk spinning round, now still forever. She turned each page slowly and when she got to the middle she stopped. Sighed, ran her hand over the protective film on the ten by eight of him as a young man in a cable fishing sweater.

'This one's my favourite. Look,' she smiled, 'he looks just like a normal guy.'

The clock kept ticking. Lisa-Marie did not come. I walked home thinking about Lisa-Marie's mam and the King. It surprised me, that Lisa-Marie's mam named her daughter after the off-spring of her rival. Maybe she was creating similarities between herself and the woman who ended up with him.

At the park the swings swayed loosely and lonely as I walked by. I needed to talk to Lisa and did not know about what in particular. Sometimes it seemed Lisa-Marie had better friends than me. Tonight she was cheating on me with God.

For once I can't remember what Madonna is wearing or doing when she sings.

Lisa-Marie stood in front of the life-size Madonna on the back of my door and turned sideways, imitating the same pose.

'What do you think?'

It was the dress, so new you could see the holes in the cotton where the tags had been.

'How come?'

Lisa wasn't someone who got new clothes without a reason. Neither of us were.

'It's for the confirmation. My dad got me it.'

'It's nice.'

I'd thought it would be different, if not an actual wedding dress, at least a Laura Ashley dress with a crisp lace collar and a cardigan to church it up a bit. This dress was lemon, short, tight with a sloppy elasticated waist hung over tight hips. Lisa-Marie raised her arms, and displayed the tea-bag vents at the side of the top, where if you were looking you could see her bra.

'Nice one. Aren't you supposed to save it till confirmation?'

'Yeah, that's why I've got this.'

She flung a grandma skirt from the top of her bag.

'I had to put this over to get out the house.'

She'd done it a million times, reached the park and stepped out of her street skirt, to emerge in something her sister wouldn't let her borrow underneath. I did the same when I wanted to wear the denim skirt my mother said I'd grown out of. If you went behind the hill, no one could see. But Lisa-Marie laughed at this – said there was no point in looking for privacy to expose clothes you were going to have on all night anyway. She had a point, but there was something about getting my legs out I needed a moment for.

'Are you wearing this?' She pulled my red and black jacket off the door.

'No, I was going for the pink one.'

She slipped on the coat and zipped herself into it, tossed her jacket and left it flailing on my bed.

It was a long walk. Up the road, over the bridge, up the hill to the posh houses.

'Do you wanna play what could happen?' I said.

What could happen wasn't really a game. It was just something we always talked about – where you could meet the love of your life, what he would be like, the perfect location and time you'd finally do it.

'I can't be arsed,' she said. 'Anyway, we're almost there.'

We stood outside the house with all the lights on, steamed windows and a dancing Coke can jiggling in the porch. Lisa-Marie took out the piece of paper and looked at the gate and back at the paper, before she slipped it back into her pocket.

'This is it.'

'Don't leave me on my own,' I said. 'Promise?'

She reached over to the bell and pressed. Boothie's mate opened the door, and we walked in.

'Boothie's not here yet,' he said. 'Do you want a drink?'

The room was full of people we didn't recognise. *So Macho* rattling the china dogs on a nick-nack shelf above the stereo. Lads huddled round a ZX Spectrum, waiting for a gorilla to throw barrels, the odd girl looking over their shoulders as they climbed the ladder to the next level.

'What have you got?' said Lisa.

'You name it.'

He looked at me with sleepy eyes, one hand patting my shoulder as he ushered us to the couch.

'A half of vodka and orange,' Lisa said.

'How about you?'

I looked at Lisa and said, 'Coke.'

Lisa looked at me, rolling her eyes.

'I don't know what I like.'

'No problem, ladies, leave it to me. I'll bring you something nice.'

He came back with two glasses, one purple, one orange.

'No Coke left,' he said. 'I brought you something better.'

I looked at Lisa, running her finger round the rim of her glass and taking a sip.

My drink tasted of blackcurrant, pink foam on top he'd drawn a heart in. I smashed the foam up with my lip, and took a sip of the now vapor-trail heart as he folded himself onto the couch next to me, sitting next to Lisa.

'My dog's got cancer. Do you wanna see it? Here girl...'

He tapped his fingers on the floor and a small ball of hair with curly bits came running.

Then he scooped up the dog and placed it on his knee, tickling its belly till it turned round.

'Here,' he said, 'put your fingers there. See it? It's the size of a fist.'

'Is it dying?' Lisa asked.

'The vet said we should put her to sleep, but look how happy she is!'

He took my fingers and ran them across the dog's bald belly. Warm. Soft skin with lead underneath. The dog wagged its tail, panted. Lisa's eyes scanned the room instead of looking at me.

'He'll be here in a bit,' said Lee.

'I'm not bothered if he turns up or not,' she shrugged.

We were onto our third drink. Time had passed slowly, now it seemed to chase its tail with smears of light and sound. A Beswick pig on the shelf, a pixelated car going too fast, when I came back from the toilet Lisa was listening to what Lee was saying. He'd already showed us his appendix scar, a burn on his arm, his elbow that popped in and out the socket on command.

'Are you nervous?' said Lee, placing his hand on Lisa's ankle.

'No,' said Lisa, looking right at him.

He slipped his long hand up to Lisa's knee. A few of the lads were looking from the ZX circle, the black box with a rainbow peeling off at one end just in view.

'Are you nervous?' he said.

'No.'

His hand moved further onto her new dress thigh.

'Are you nervous?'

She hesitated as she saw me approach.

'Howay, I thought you were game?'

Lee's hand moved away as she crossed her legs, and I sat down.

'He's here!'

Lee looked over at the door, Boothie raising his hand as he walked in, pointing to the kitchen.

Lisa swigged the rest of her drink.

'Just going for a top-up,' she said as she walked away.

Through the patio doors I could see them, as I stood up. Lemon cotton, a bomber jacket. Sea of bodies in the way, as they closed the door behind them and walked into the garden.

She'd been gone forever.

As I came out the bathroom he was standing there.

'There you are. I was wondering where you'd got to.'

I stepped towards the stairs slowly, hand tracing the wall. A picture of a handsome man in a uniform looking back at me. Or else just a young man in a uniform that lent him the word handsome.

'He's away.'

He grabbed my hand and my feet followed as he opened a door, whispered, 'This is his room.'

The room was grey. White-and-red-striped duvet. Girls on the walls. And two or three half-finished model aeroplanes.

It started to rain outside, but not so you could hear it. Not so much you could really see it except the odd sparkle on the glass.

'Are you nervous?' he said. Cold hands through my jeans.

The streetlights made orange beads on the glass, pinprick colours. Somewhere outside Lisa was drinking fresh orange with vodka from a tumbler.

I shook my head.

He moved his hand.

On mine his lips were a wet and dry vacuum cleaner, sucking and making a seal over my skin. Lisa and me would have so much to talk about. So much we could be one and the same.

'Are you nervous?' he said.

I wondered what Lisa would do. If she'd gone inside yet, felt the rain yet on her confirmation cotton.

I shook my head, and he turned out the light. Closed my eyes.

Somewhere she was outside. And Madge was on the wall, in the dark, with her eyes open wide.

Madonna was sending me mixed messages. Some days guys were angels, who thawed your snow with one look, stars that shone light into the darkness. Love is a fancy-dress costume, something you could dress almost anyone up in. Other days it was immaterial. It's the last track from an album of mostly love songs when she tells you it's a lie after all. Love is a hotel room with a neon sign flashing in the window long after the paid guests have gone.

Lisa took my hand in hers, then the other. Held them steady.

'It's a new version,' she said.

I nodded.

Madonna slumped against the hi-fi, satin gloves extended, not touching a thing.

'Have you ever been poked?'

I shook my head.

'Been licked out?'

'No.'

'Had missionary sex?'

Nuns in white-and-black penguin hats, lying on their backs and looking at the trees.

'No.'

'Gobbled?'

Chickens competing for a feed.

'No.'

'Doggy style?'

'Up the arse?'

'Standing up?'

'69er?'

A dyslexic 99 cone, photo on the side of the van. Monkeys' blood dripping down the sides of your flake to ice cream.

Then she said, 'Have you ever been round the world?'

I shook my head again, neither caring or asking what it meant.

Seems you never pass the test, there's always the next level left to go.

No one had played Madonna all night. It was that kind of party.

Outside. everything was clear. The rain had made everything slick and bright.

'I couldn't find you,' she said. 'Where were you all that time?'

'Nowhere. He was just asking about you, he's secretly in love with you, I think.'

The words slipped out. I wondered why later. Why I felt like that woman in *EastEnders* who cheated on her husband, why I didn't want to tell her anything when I couldn't tell her everything, why I felt like that woman who was having what they call an affair.

She smiled, linked her arm in mine as we crossed the street.

'It's my confirmation on Sunday, if you wanna come. It'll be a laugh.'

She pulled the collar of the jacket up and snuggled down into it, hands deep inside the terry toweling pockets, holding close and making my coat her own.

We walked home slowly down the empty street, her heels making clicks as they stepped in and out of oil-slick traffic lights smeared into the path. Amber, green, red. Right up the road I could see them changing without a car in sight. No one but me standing at the curb, patiently waiting to cross.

Too Many Love Songs

By Paul Summers

'... my faith for you is as wide and steady as a Texan moon'
'The Well', Jennifer Warnes

1. (How Little It Matters) How Little We Know - Frank Sinatra

he is skimming pebbles
through rip-tides: each
cold, flat stone, skipping
the sea's relentless beats.

on the grey beach at easter,
the young lovers kiss;
their first in daylight,
sober, after nervous breakfasts.

above them, the clouds fidget.

2. A Case Of You - Joni Mitchell

let's go to safeway, she said,
let's get married, said he,
half asking, half telling
& all but drowned out
by the drone of the washer;
& she carried on with the shopping list
& he dreamed about a sunny hill,
a derelict temple, scorched white,
inhabited only by a family of doves:
& she asked if they needed cornflakes,
& he promised his love at the altar
of an unpronounceable goddess,
his entire body beaming with truth.

do you need some more coffee?
she said, & he answered, i do,
with all the life in my heart, i do.

& so they were married
between the cereal
& the soap-powder,
her not really knowing
& him knowing too well.

3. Blame It On The Sun - Stevie Wonder

steve, her brother, is *staying neutral*.
he's just here to shift her gear.

he bends his legs, lifts, negotiates
the landing's odd geometry:

& the last straining box of her intricate
follies heads out to the van.

so that's it then? onwards & upwards?
brave new worlds?

i suppose a last-minute reconciliation
is out of the question?

a tall order even for them,
those agents of fortune dudes,
whoever the fuck they might be?

4. I Want You - Elvis Costello

i had all but forgotten
her face;

our blunt goodbyes,
as black & irreparable
as her smeared mascara:
verse after verse
of unutterable truth,
her chorus of daggers
let fly, like a skyful
of starlings, as dense
as guinness.

the old man opposite
weaves another tale;
& me still unravelling
his parable of the talented.

tell me again what she said.

5. What Is This? - Bobby Womack

i remember it all
the air hot as a fever
the universe slow and fat
3 red flowers
an old tree blazes green
in brilliant concrete
champagne clouds
smoke dance
sailing like ghost angels
in the broken morning
the porcelain woman
is naked by the window
her belly like warm marble

eyes, strong coffee
wild as an ocean
i drink in their softness
my heart misses a beat

6. Still In Love With You - Thin Lizzy

as if all she had ever been
or could be was a photograph
she fires that broadside glance
black & white & grainy
as a hilltop in thick drizzle
a *dr zhivago* out-take
the gentle arch of her lips
a slumped roman bridge

i remember the birch forest
a thatch of shadows & snow
the steam rising like genies
from the curve of her back
as if all she had ever been
or could be was forever.

7. Let's Get It On - Marvin Gaye

me and marvin stayed in
spent the whole weekend
worshipping your debris
hours just smiling
at the wreckage of the duvet
even the prospect of there
never being a socialist revolution
could not annoy me
nor the thought of the spartans
being cheated out of a home tie
with arsenal back in '78

not even the knowledge that mam
thinks all my poems are weird
and dad never once said well played
already I will love your smiles
forever

8. I Think I'll Call It Morning – Gil Scott-Heron

when you pulled on your tights
you looked a picture

leaning on the edge of morning

i mention the beauty of it
& you blush

half hidden now
by the silk of your camisole

9. Ain't That Love – Ray Charles

today in the warm grip of spring sun
i hear the tick of the moving shadows,
think of eternity, of great stones reduced
to dust, of lazy hills shifting their contours,
the greedy sea reclaiming its birthright.

i see us – there in a bus-stop, a car-park,
on a quiet bench near an avenue of trees;
back-lit by rose sunsets. our hair has grown
the colour of snow, our skin turned to paper,
but still our fingers knotted in gentle union.

we take alternate licks from a shared ice cream,
nuzzle like hungry calves, revelling in the moment's
warmth; we steal a smoochy waltz, a slow kiss
in gaps between the strangers gaze & passing cars;
without complacency for the blackbird's serenade,

133

the late hyacinth's rich scent, the worth of mutual
tears at some sad movie, the sheer joy of gene kelly
stomping in silver puddles. i have never carried your
photograph in my wallet – never needed to; your face
etched as it is in fifty poses on the lining of my eyelids.

10. Song For Bernadette – Jennifer Warnes

we are digging graves for our dreams
a cold tumour of cloud spitting its bridle
throws an obese cherub from its back

thunder succumbing to twisted reason
the ghost-child pockets pearls of frozen dew
fragile grass dissolving to powdered jade

blue moonlight barcodes through the birch
anoxic fingers cupping us in their desperate grip
see the brick shattered by a single night of frost

a concave heaven reflected
in the newness of our spades

11. Tupelo Honey – Van Morrison

the infinite romance of a sideways glance, your bedtime eyes,
your tv trance, the halo of your crimson lips when sculpted by a mock surprise
that random curl beneath your ear, the laughter line which tracks your tear
your love of the skies we lie beneath, the little gaps between your teeth.

12. My Beautiful Friend - The Charlatans

sweat-stuck sand in a heart tattoo
on the small of your back

ashkenazi ringlets set in jet springs
candied by the salt of a coral sea

a dirty ibis breaks the honey sky
sometimes i imagine the gaps you'd leave

The Road and the Miles to Dundee

By Val McDermid

I hate this dress. It's lemon yellow with blue roses and it makes my skin look like semolina pudding, my cheeks like dauds of strawberry jam in the middle of the plate. This dress, it's Bri-nylon and it cuts in under my arms and it makes me sweat. I hate the crackly white petticoat that's sewn in. It's like plastic, scratchy and rustly. You can hear me coming halfway across the town. Mostly, though, I hate it because it's a hand-me-down. It belonged to my cousin Morag whom I'm supposed to like because she's my cousin and she's only a year older than me, but I hate her too. She's a clipe, always telling tales. She's a Moaning Minnie. And she's boring. And I get the horrible clothes Auntie Betty makes for her after she's outgrown them. And they never fit because she's a beanpole and I'm not. But I have to wear them. According to my mum, they're too good to throw away. Me, I'd build a bonfire and set light to the lot of them.

It's my big cousin Senga's twenty-first, which is why I'm wearing the party dress. We're all crammed into my Auntie Jean's living-room, and the adults are all red in the face and cheery with the drink. This is my first grown-up party, and I'm supposed to be pleased that I've been allowed to come and stay up past my bedtime. But there's nothing to do and nobody to talk to. I can't even torment Morag because she's not here. Auntie Betty made her stay at home because it's too late for a big jessie like Morag to be up, even though she's eleven and I'm only ten. Next time I see her, I'll tell her how great it was. She willnae know it's a lie.

I'm that fed up I've made myself a den. I'm sitting under the table with a tumbler of lemonade and a bowl of crisps I sneaked away when nobody was looking. I've never had crisps like this before. They're sort of square and very yellow and if you look at them really close up, they've got lots of tiny wee bubbles under the surface. They don't even taste like crisps. When I suck them, they sort of burst on my tongue and taste of cheese and salt, not potatoes. The bag they came in said, 'Marks & Spencer Savoury Crisps', so I thought they'd be all right. I'm not really sure if I like them or not. But I'm bored, so I'm eating them just the same.

Somebody turns off the record player and now it's time for people to do their party pieces. Auntie Jean first, just as soon as she's finished telling off Uncle Tom for not refilling her rum and coke quick enough. She's always telling Uncle Tom off for something. I feel sorry for him. I thought it was only bairns that got picked on like she picks on him. I thought when you were a grown-up, folk stopped bothering you.

Anyway, Auntie Jean's got her rum and Coke and she's away. Eyes shut, swaying a wee bit with the emotion. She always used to sing *Grannie's Hielan' Hame*, but lately she's taken to that Julie Rogers song, *The Wedding*. Maybe she's trying to tell Senga something. Her voice is rusty with fags, but she belts it out all the same. 'And I can hear sweet voices singing, Ave Mar-ee-hee-haa.' Dad says when God was handing out voices, Auntie Jean was in the lavvy. When she finishes, everybody whoops and cheers. I don't know why, unless it's relief because it's over.

Then it's my dad. I squirm around under the table so I can see him better. He plants his feet a wee bit apart and squares his shoulders in his good grey suit. I know what's coming. *The Road and the Miles to Dundee* is his song. Nobody else would dare sing it. Apart from anything else, it would just make them look stupid, because my dad's got a great voice. He's as good as Kenneth McKellar. Everybody says so. He clears his throat and out comes that sweet voice that makes me feel like I'm snuggled up someplace safe and warm.

Cauld winter was howlin' o'er moor and o'er mountain
And wild was the surge of the dark rolling sea,
When I met about daybreak a bonnie young lassie,
Wha asked me the road and the miles to Dundee.

He's on the last verse when everything goes wrong. Without thinking about it, I've eased out from under the table to hear better. And that's when that evil witch Auntie Betty spots me. My dad's just coming to the end of the song when she bellows like a bullock. 'My God, have you ett that whole bowl of crisps yoursel'? Nae wonder you've got all that puppy fat on you.'

I want to die. Instead of looking at my dad, everybody's looking at me. The last note dies away, and though a few folk are clapping, mostly they're eyeing up the yellow lemon dress straining at the seams. I can see them thinking, 'Greedy wee shite', as clearly as if they had cartoon thought bubbles over their heads. I want to shout out and tell them I just look fat because it's not my dress.

There's a horrible moment of hush. Then suddenly my dad's feet appear in front of my face. 'Leave the bairn alone, Betty,' he says in a different voice from the one we've all been listening to. This one's hard and quiet, the one I know never to argue with.

But Auntie Betty's stupid as well as evil. 'Jim, I'm only speaking for her own good,' she says, and I can hear exactly where Morag gets her slimy ways fi'.

'Betty,' my dad says, 'You've always been an interfering bitch. Now leave my bairn alone.'

Auntie Betty flushes scarlet and retreats, muttering something nobody's listening to. There's a flurry of movement and Uncle Don launches into *The Mucking o' Geordie's Byre*. My dad drops to the floor beside me, says nothing, puts his hand over mine.

My hero.

Says I, 'My young lassie, I canna' weel tell ye
The road and the distance I canna' weel gie.
But if you'll permit me tae gang a wee bittie,
I'll show ye the road and the miles to Dundee.'
At once she consented and gave me her arm,
Ne'er a word did I speir wha the lassie micht be,
She appeared like an angel in feature and form,
As she walked by my side on the road to Dundee.

* * *

I'm off to university in a couple of days. I'm really excited, but I'm a bit scared too. I'm off to England. I've only ever been there twice before – the first time, a holiday in Blackpool when I was eleven, the second my university interview. Both times, I felt like I'd been transported to another planet. Now my life as an alien is about to begin, and I can't wait to get away and dive into this new world. I can be anybody I want to be. I can make myself up from scratch.

But for now, I'm still trapped in who I've always been. This time next week, I'll be in the shadow of Oxford's dreaming spires, drinking coffee with intellectuals, talking about politics and ideas and literature. Tonight, though, I'm at Dysart Miners' Welfare for my cousin Senga's spree. She's marrying an Englishman. 'I don't suppose they have sprees in England,' I say to him.

'No,' he says. There's something about the way he says it that makes me think he's another one who's feeling like his life as an alien is only just beginning.

The show of presents is at the far end of the hall, a row of trestle tables covered in white paper, groaning under the weight of china, linen, glassware and the strange assortment of things people think newlyweds need for a proper start in life. There's a whole subsection entirely devoted to Pyrex casseroles. My cousin Derry whispers to me that Hutt's department store had a special offer on Pyrex last month, that's why there are twenty-three of them on display. 'Do you think they'll be able to swap them?' I ask.

'Christ, I hope so,' he says. 'Otherwise we'll all be getting Pyrex for Christmas.'

The demarcation lines are clearly drawn. The women sit at tables round the perimeter of the hall, leaving a space in the middle for the dancing. The men congregate round the long bar that occupies most of one side of the room. I'm already getting the hard stare from Auntie Betty and her cronies for standing with the men at the bar, drinking underage pints and smoking. Morag is staring wistfully across at me, like she wishes she had the nerve to come and join me and Derry and Senga's fiancé. But she won't budge. She hasn't got a rebellious molecule in her body.

The band's been playing a wee while now, and a few folk have been dancing, but nothing much is happening. 'Is it no' time for a wee song, Jim?' one of the other men asks my dad.

'Aye, you're probably right. I'll away up and have a word with the bandleader.' It's a grandiose term for the leader of the trio of accordion, drums and guitar that have been serenading us with a competent if uninspired selection of Scottish standards and pop songs from the previous decade. But my dad walks up to the stage anyway and leans over the accordionist, his mouth close to the wee bald man's ear.

When they finish their rendition of *The Bluebell Polka*, my dad steps up to the microphone. 'Ladies and gentlemen, the band has kindly agreed that they'll accompany anybody who wants to give us a song. So if you don't mind, I'll start off the proceedings.' And he's off. The familiar words float above the band and he treats us to his usual graceful rendition.

But tonight, I'm not in the mood. I'm not Daddy's wee lassie any more. I'm a young woman on the threshold of her life, and I don't want to acquiesce quietly to anything. He finishes the song and, by popular demand, gives us an encore of *Ae Fond Kiss*.

By the time he gets back to the bar, Auntie Jean is up there, belting out *The Wedding* with all the smug complacency of a woman who has got the difficult daughter boxed off on the road to the aisle. My dad takes a welcome swallow of his lager and smiles at me.

I scowl in return. 'Does it not strike you as a wee bit hypocritical, you singing that song?' I say.

He looks baffled. 'What?'

'It's all about a man who takes pity on a lassie who's trying to get to Dundee. Right? He helps her. With no thought of anything in return. Right?' I demand.

'Aye,' he says cautiously. The last year or two have taught him caution is a good policy when it comes to crossing verbal swords with me. I've learned a lot from the school debating society, and even more from the students in Edinburgh I hang out with at weekends.

'And you don't find anything hypocritical in that?'

'No,' he says. 'He does the right thing, the fellow in the song.'

'So how come you won't pick up hitchhikers, then?' I say.

Game, set and match.

At length wi' the Howe o' Strathmartine behind us,
The spires o' the toon in full view we could see,
She said 'Gentle Sir, I can never forget ye
For showing me far on the road to Dundee'.

I took the gowd pin from the scarf on my bosom
And said 'Keep ye this in remembrance o' me'
Then bravely I kissed the sweet lips o' the lassie,
E'er I parted wi' her on the road to Dundee.

* * *

I'm staying with my friend Antonia and her husband, who have a house on the shores of Lake Champlain, a long finger of water that forms part of the border between Vermont and New York State. Antonia and I became friends at Oxford, in spite of the difference in our backgrounds. She was a diplomat's daughter, educated at public school, born to privilege and position. And it didn't matter a damn because we were equals in the things that mattered.

We're having a good time. This feels like the life I've always wanted. My first book is due to be published in a week's time, I'm travelling the world, young, free and single, and I have appropriated Antonia's sense of entitlement with not a premonition of what might change that. I'm swimming in the chilly dark waters of Lake Champlain when it happens, though I'm oblivious to it the time. We come out of the water and run up to the house, our only thought how soon we can get dried off and settle in front of the log fire with a glass of good malt whisky.

It's the middle of the night when I find out my life has changed irrevocably. I drift out of sleep, woken by a distant phone ringing. I turn over and set my compass for unconsciousness when Antonia is suddenly standing in front of me, her face crumpled and distressed. 'The phone... it's for you.' I can't make sense of this but I roll out of bed and go downstairs anyway. Her husband is standing mute, the receiver held out to me.

The voice on the other end is familiar. 'I'm awful sorry, lassie,' says Uncle Tom. 'It's your dad. He was playing bowls. He walked out on the green to play the final of the tournament. And he just dropped down dead.' His voice keeps going, but I can't make out the words.

Later that day, I'm walking in the rain in Central Park. Antonia has organised everything; a flight from Burlington to New York, then a night flight back to Scotland via Paris. I've packed my bags, but I've still got four hours to kill. So I buy my first packet of cigarettes in years and walk. Smoke and rain, good excuses for a wet face and red eyes. The dye in my passport runs as I get soaked to the skin; for years, I can't escape remembrance of this day every time I travel abroad.

It's taken them a couple of days to track me down, so I don't get back till the day of the funeral. The crematorium is packed, standing-room only for a man so many people loved. The minister's doing a good job – he knew my dad, so he understands the need to celebrate a life as well as mourn a death. He actually makes us laugh, and I think of my dad watching all this from somewhere else and maybe realising how much his life meant.

Back at the house, after the formal funeral purvey, it's family only. I'm in the kitchen with our Senga making potted meat sandwiches. I feel dazed. I'm not sure whether it's grief or jetlag or what. I'm taking the bread knife to a tall stack of sandwiches, cutting them into neat triangles, when Auntie Betty barges into the kitchen. She puts a hand on my shoulder and says, 'Are you awful upset about your dad, then?'

It's a question so crass I can't believe she's uttered it. I feel Senga's hand gently easing the bread knife from mine. Just as well, really. I stare mutely at Auntie Betty, wishing with my whole heart that it was her burned to ash instead of my dad.

Senga says, 'If you don't mind, Auntie Betty, there's not really room for three people in here and we need to get the sandwiches done.'

Auntie Betty edges backwards. 'Right enough,' she says. 'I just thought I'd come and tell you Simon's going to give us a wee song.'

Simon is the late baby, born when Morag was twelve. There has never been a child more beautiful, more intelligent, more gifted. Well, that's what Auntie Betty thinks. Personally, I prefer another set of adjectives – spoilt, arrogant, average. His thin, reedy tenor makes me yearn for Auntie Jean singing *The Wedding*.

'Aye,' Betty continues. 'He's going to give us *The Road and the Miles to Dundee*.'

I feel the blood draining from my face and the room loses focus. I push her out of the way and head for the front door, grabbing my jacket as I run. I tear from the house and jump into the car, not caring that I've had more whisky than the law allows drivers. At first, I'm not thinking about where I'm going, but my heart knows what it needs, and it's not my cousin Simon murdering my father's favourite song. I drive out of town and up into the hills. These days, you can drive almost all the way up Falkland Hill. But it didn't use to be like that. The first time I climbed it was the night before my sixth birthday. My mum wanted me out of the way so she could ice the cake, and my dad took me up the hill. It felt like a mountain to my child's legs; it felt like achievement. We stood on the top, looking down at Fife, my world, spread beneath our feet like a magic carpet.

Now, twenty-six years later, I'm here again. I want music. I finger the tape of my dad singing that one of his friends from the Bowhill People's Burns Club's concert party pressed into my hand as I left the crematorium. 'I made a wee compilation for you,' he said, his eyes damp with sorrow.

But I'm not ready for this. Instead, I slam the Mozart Requiem into the tape player, roll down the windows, turn the volume up full and stand on the hillside, staring out at the blurry view. I know the world is still at my feet.

The difference is that today, I don't want it.

So here's to the lassie, I ne'er can forget her,
And ilka young laddie that's listening to me,
O never be sweer to convoy a young lassie
Though it's only to show her the road to Dundee.

* * *

I'm thirty thousand feet above somewhere. I don't much care where. I'm flying to a festival to read from my work in a country I can't point to on a map. I'm flying away from the ending of the relationship I never expected to die. My life feels ragged and wrecked, my heart torn and trampled. It's as if the last dozen years have been folded up tight like tissue paper, turning into a hard lump that could stick in my throat and choke me.

I take out the book I've brought as a bulwark against the strangling gyre of my thoughts. Ali Smith's *The Whole Story and Other Stories*. I chose it deliberately in preference to a novel because I can't actually concentrate for long enough to manage more than bite-sized chunks.

A few stories in, I start reading one called *Scottish Love Songs*. It's magical and strange, tragic and funny, but most of all, it's an affirmation of the power and endurance of love. A bitter irony that I'm far from immune to. I'm bearing up well until the pipers in the story start playing *The Road and the Miles to Dundee*. Then I become that person that nobody wants to sit next to on the plane, the one with the fat tears rolling down her cheeks and the trumpeting nose-blowing that shocks even the screaming toddler in the next row into silence.

Two nights later, I'm lying in a bed in a city in the middle of Europe, limbs entangled with a virtual stranger. We're in that charmed place between satisfactory sex and the recognition that we probably don't have much to say to each other. I don't know why, but I start to tell her about the incident on the plane, and all the other memories associated with *The Road and the Miles to Dundee*. I don't expect much response; I recall once writing that casual lovers are like domestic pets – you can almost believe they understand every word you say.

But I'm pleasantly surprised. She shifts her long legs so she can more readily face me, pushes her tawny hair out of her eyes and frowns in concentration. At one point, when I pause, searching for the next point in the narrative, her hand moves to my hip and she says, 'Go on. This is interesting.'

I come to the end of what I have to say and she traces my mouth with a fingertip. 'Sad,' she says. Then shakes her head. 'No, strike that. Sad's too small a word. Too simple.'

But simplification is what I need. I suddenly understand that I want to strip away every association from this damn song except the sweetness of my father's voice. I don't know how to express this, but somehow, this woman grasps the essence without being told. 'It's a love song,' she says. 'You need to remember that. You need to replace the bad connections with good ones.'

'Easier said than done,' I sigh. I want to change the subject, so I choose something else to occupy our mouths. It's sweet, this encounter. It doesn't touch the core of my pain, but it reminds me that sooner or later, there will be mitigation.

Three days later, we detach from each other in the departure lounge, heading for different provincial airports. We've made no plans to meet again, mostly because I've headed her off at the pass every time.

I'm only home an hour when there's a ring at the doorbell. I'm not expecting anyone, but of all the people I'm not expecting, the florist would come high on the list. But she's there, presenting me with a dozen yellow roses. Puzzled, I check they're really for me and not the woman next door. The florist smiles at my distrust. 'No, they're really for you,' she says. 'There's a card. I hope I got the spelling right.'

I close the door and walk slowly through to the kitchen. I wriggle the card free from the cellophane wrapping and tear open the envelope. I read the words, and I can't keep the big silly smile from my face.

'O never be sweer to convoy a young lassie,
Though it's only to show her the road to Dundee.'

The phone's ringing, and I have a funny feeling it's going to be a voice asking for directions.

Morning Strength

By Barrie Darke

By the age of fourteen, it had been settled that Reba was forbidden to see boys. Her stepdad declared this; her real mother agreed. At first it hadn't bothered Reba much – she thought they were overestimating her sociability.

She never worked out why it was she noticed the milkman. Some click in her head or her guts, something to do with her age, she supposed, when she did think about it later. His round took him by the school before the first bell rang, and because he was barely over school-leaving age himself, and not immediately fanciable, a group of girls ripped into him most dry mornings. He struggled to look amused, and never said anything back.

Reba, who chose not to join groups, observed this for a week. Then at three o'clock one morning she held her breath on her way downstairs and left a note between the empty bottles outside the door. This note contained some musings on those girls. An hour later, when the motor and the bottle rattle came, she knelt up in bed and put her elbows on the cold windowsill. It was November outside.

He came quickly up the path, and she lost sight of him at the door; then he stepped back, scanned the windows. They exchanged what turned out to be grim little half-smiles. A few hours later at the school gates, they found the same smiles came in useful again.

That night Reba went to bed at her normal time and lay for a few hours before rising and dressing warmly. She sat in the dark downstairs, picturing the changing expressions of sleep above her. When the metallic noise arrived, surely louder than usual, she took her mother's keys from the telephone table and dealt with the front door. He was on the next garden path, and didn't seem surprised to see her. They nodded. She sat in the milk float, watching her breath, trying not to look back at the house. If any lights came on, she didn't want to know.

He said his name was Jason. He swung himself into the seat behind the wheel without looking at it, and had the float moving before his back hit the upright. When they left her street behind, she felt a light blue chill of nerves, but it passed when he started talking.

146

His speech was interrupted every few minutes by the deliveries, but his words were never disjointed. Reba was concerned about the everyday volume of his voice, but he must've been aware of what he could get away with. He talked about their school, which he had left three years ago after a below-average stint. He thought it important to debunk some of the myths about the teachers that she hadn't really believed anyway: that the PE teacher had been in prison for murder early in his life, that the French teacher's son had been left paralysed in a playground fight in the 80s, that the art teacher had once exposed her breasts at a school disco.

There was no pressure on Reba to talk, so she didn't, much. The new streets took most of her attention. Cats were plentiful, and seemed as free as it was possible to be on this planet. She thought she saw a squirrel, but maybe not, and Jason mentioned he regularly saw a tortoise escaping from someone's jungly garden. She was surprised and depressed by how many houselights were switching on at almost five o'clock. There were car engine sounds from other streets, and firm door slams, but that first morning they didn't see a soul.

At six o'clock he lent her some money – she hadn't thought to bring any – and dropped her off at a bus stop. He was quiet for the first time as she stepped down. Reba asked if it was all right to come out again the next morning. He shrugged, nodded, said he had to be careful, but yeah.

She was the only one on the bus, and the driver didn't say anything. Her presence at this hour only confirmed something hard in his worldview. A couple of stops before hers, an old workman heaved himself on and fell asleep as soon as he stumbled to his seat. The bus stopped behind her street, but first passed along the top of it. She squinted at the windows for those few seconds. There were no police lights down there.

To get back in, she had to cross the field behind the house. This placed her in full view of the back bedroom windows, but no curtains were moving, there were no glows, it was all easier than she'd thought. Lying in bed again, her hair smelt of fresh air, and she expected her nose was a red beacon, but these were things that would fade. At seven prompt, bedroom and bathroom doors started opening.

The milk round included the houses of some fellow pupils. One was a boy named Reece, who, in Reba's view, suffered from a confidence born of having a fraction more money in the family than was usual. So one morning she stepped out of the float and stood at his gate; then she walked up the path with no clue what came next. The curtains were drawn so she couldn't see all the things the family had. Jason was quickly back in the float, giving no sign he thought this was wrong of her. The only thing Reba had to hand was the damp grass on the lawn, so she tore up a slippery handful and scraped it as best she could through the letterbox.

At school five hours later she had to be careful not to excite comment by scrutinising Reece. She didn't know what she'd hoped for – a slight paleness, a tremor in his hands maybe – but there was no sign of anything. She doubted he was the first up in that household.

Two nights passed uneventfully, and then they saw an old-style tramp sitting on the ground, round and red in the face, silver bristles catching the moonlight. He wore the expected layers of drab clothes, but also a black trilby, with a beige scarf that looked new tied around his throat. He was collapsed against a low garden wall, but when the float disturbed him he rolled over and pushed himself up with thick hands. As he billowed forward, his shoes dragged across the road, and Reba thought: he should pick his feet up, he'll wear his heels down.

Jason explained that the old man thought it was the 1940s and the war was on – he liked throwing milk bottles up at the sky to stop the Nazi planes bombing his loved ones. Hands were already flailing for the crates when Jason stepped down and punched him three times in the face, three flicks to stop him coming forward, to drive him back, to roll him over into sleep. Jason braved a hand under each armpit to drag him back to his spot against the wall. Then he began the deliveries.

That same night they passed an area where all the streetlights were off and a few alarms were sounding. Jason said it was a power cut, happened more often than you'd think. The streets were a thick countryside black like Reba had never seen before: gardens more suited to this than electric light and shadows, and she thought how disturbing the night-time would've been hundreds of years before, how much of a justification for every superstition you could think of.

Jason mentioned all the clock radios that would be awry, all the videos failing to tape show-off foreign films, all the rusty body clocks that would have to be relied on.

On the Thursday morning of that first week, Jason told her where the PE teacher lived, he who was said to have strangled a taxi driver on the way home from his 21st birthday, and since they'd made good time they could afford a little detour. Reba posted some grass through the door, but heard a dog snuffling and padding forward while her fingers were still fluttering in the letterbox, and then there was a shattering bark. They were gone in no time, but Reba saw over her shoulder that lights had come on in the house. She could hardly sit still on the bus home that morning, and wanted someone to talk to about it. She span round in circles when she crossed the field behind the house, all the doors closed behind her hard enough to make her wince, and she was close to a giggling fit when she got ready for bed.

She watched the PE teacher, out in the cold field that morning. She thought she detected signs he was feeling his age.

Sleep became a problem. At first she'd thought that, once she was home from school, she'd be able to spread short naps through the evening's schedule of family moments, making up enough ground to be fresh for three o'clock in the morning and the twenty or so hours following it. But she couldn't drop off if she knew it wasn't going to be for an eight-hour stretch; it was especially difficult when she considered the suspicions her napping would raise.

So by the end of the first week she noticed the slow cave-in, the sensation of cool melting. Ulcers began studding her mouth and her body set up a low-frequency vibration that seemed to threaten a total shutdown. She couldn't walk through a door without banging a shoulder off the frame, and her mind refused to consider more than one gummy thought at a time. The wooden school desks, if she looked at them long enough, became confused with the wooden furniture they had at home, and she often thought during a slow lesson that she was back there, could go to the fridge for a can of Coke at any time. If somebody spoke to her, she stared at them for far too long before she managed to respond. Her eyes were bloodshot and darkened in a way, however, that she didn't mind too much.

At home in the mornings, it was easy to cover. Reba was at her freshest, and her parents were at their least observant as they gathered their strengths to face the day. But one evening her constant yawning was commented on, and led to a befuddled talk on the kind of bad dreams keeping her awake. She said they'd been doing the concentration camps in history, which shut everyone up.

The one she remembered best was the crying woman with the suitcase. This was at half-past five, a blonde in her forties, heavy and weatherbeaten, leaning to one side as she hurried along the path. She was oblivious to them seeing the mascara running off her chin. Jason stayed on the float, but Reba got down, asked the woman what was the matter. But the woman didn't look up past her shoes. She shook her head, sidestepped Reba, juddering as she moved.

They discussed it for a while. Jason said that, at this time of night, your first ideas to explain something never fit, it was always more extreme, three or four thoughts along. So it could've been she was suffering from a new form of Alzheimer's that touched the early middle-aged and she believed she would find her childhood home around the next corner, then the next; or she had finally left her husband, but her adulterous lover wanted to celebrate by having her take a dump on his chest, and now she was going back to tell the husband it was all a dream he'd been having; or it was that her recently murdered teenage daughter was haunting her, forcing her to go out in the small hours and find happiness at the lower end of humanity. That last one was Reba's, but she was too tired to make much of it.

In the middle of the second week they passed a house belonging to a girl called Helen from school. She was from a comfortable background but tried to be one of the rough girls, who came from not so comfortable backgrounds, and ended up being neither one thing nor the other but an unpleasant thing to Reba all the same. Reba didn't bother with the grass, but she always took an evaluating look at the drowsy face of the house.

That morning, Helen was staring out of her bedroom window. It was arguable that Helen suffered the bigger shock. Reba flinched and swore but didn't duck back in her seat. There was nothing for it but to stay where she was, glancing up occasionally as if this was normality. Helen stared at her flatly. Reba waved when the float moved off.

Despite her mind being completely unglued that morning, it took Reba only two seconds to think of an answer to Helen's questions in the yard. She denied it was her in the float. She insisted that she was the one who hadn't been able to sleep, she was the one looking out of her window when the float went by – it was Helen who'd been sitting down there, and she'd been wearing a daft-looking woolly hat as well. Helen opened her mouth. Then she closed it and walked away.

Reba told Jason about that the next morning, and he laughed about it, was pleased, told her he was proud of her for that kind of thinking. She said it was being out here that did it, and she had him to thank for that. They both knew to skitter away from that kind of talk.

Reba didn't know how she heard about the house party set for the Friday night of the second week. At the most alert of times that sort of communication faded down to rumour before reaching her. Maybe it was being half asleep that did it: the normal routes of perception were silted up, so information was diverted through unused channels. Or maybe that thought itself was an example of being half asleep. Anyway, the house in question was not far off the round, and the party was going to be an all-nighter.

Jason had a tape machine with him that morning, playing ancient music, blues and country from the 20s and 30s in America. Reba imagined skeletons snapping the strings on their guitars but carrying on anyway, skeletons wearing bonnets for the women singers, gangster snap-brims for the men.

When they arrived in the party street, Jason dropped her at a corner distant enough for them to be unconnected. It was almost four o'clock and the hour was beginning to tell. People were unbalanced in the frosty garden, and those that looked at her couldn't place her – it would come to them when they woke the next afternoon, if they remembered it at all. Reba passed by everyone silently. Some were sitting far enough forward for their brows to be tickled by the stiffening grass.

The front door was so wide open it was uneasy on its hinges, and inside the house had undergone the neglect of ten years in as many hours. She wouldn't have been surprised to see sparking wires sticking out of the walls. Every window was smeared, probably from wet tampons. Underfoot were leaking cans, pizzas, and the unconscious. Some serious couples were talking about their hearts on the couches, and didn't stop for long when they saw her. In one room, boys not yet adept at talking to girls were watching a Vietnam film. In what might once have been a dining room, more confident boys and girls were taking turns blasting out songs on the hi-fi; some kind of flirtation was going on in the choices. Reba was already leaving that room when they noticed her. They couldn't be sure it was her - no one had ever seen her in anything but her school uniform - and no one followed her.

The kitchen was in the sorriest condition, someone having thrown sugar and jam around, topping off the mess with broken glass; the evening's fights had also been staged there. In the back garden, drunken boys were running at the fence and trying to jump it into the next garden, with the injuries stacking up. Upstairs, the bathroom she knew to avoid, its open door being the opposite of an invitation. The bedroom doors were closed, firmly.

Reba sat at the top of the stairs and remembered how as a child she'd bumped down them till she felt queasy. She wanted to do something significant, something that chimed with the small hours; she felt the freedom to be original before dawn came. She knew it should have something to do with the closed bedrooms, and that it should tend more towards the scary than the beautiful. But she couldn't yet work her brain up to it. She sat there for five minutes before leaving the party.

She wandered the streets slowly. She knew the route, the short cuts to catch up with Jason, but she was in no hurry, despite it being a wintry morning now. She passed through a street where the road was badly tarmacked, and noticed that the tiny frosted-over stones, the pit-holes and rubble, had the shiny blue-black look of the microscopic close-ups of insects and hair in biology textbooks.

She found Jason, told him the party had been dead. They carried on with the round, but there wasn't much time left. They almost had to race the bus to the stop.

When she got off the bus she crackled across the field, almost expected her hair to be drawing blue sparks from the air.

The family didn't have weekend lie-ins, and her stepdad was his usual sunken self. He was involved on the mechanical side in a go-karting team that took up most of his Saturday mornings, and was thinking of nothing but that over the breakfast table. Her mother, however, showed extra signs of politeness, faint but definitely there. Reba's spine prickled at this.

Her stepdad left after he'd drained his second mug. Reba sat on the couch with the remote control, trying to be interested in those programmes. Her mother soon came in, still in her dressing gown, clutching her mug of coffee. She looked straight at Reba, something that was uncomfortable nowadays, and sat down by her. Her voice was fairly small when she asked Reba to go and have a look through the kitchen window.

Reba did. The kitchen overlooked the field she had to cross every morning. There were two clear, dark lines of footprints in the frost heading for the back gate.

Reba returned to the front room. She decided not to answer any questions, though plenty came her way about the tiredness she'd been exhibiting, the extra clothes that had been appearing in the wash, the general otherworldliness of her now. In the end Reba had to get up, go to her room and lie on the bed. Her mother followed her as far as the doorway, still asking questions and making connections, only the voice was now growing shrill.

In a few hours her stepdad was back, and Reba could hear their voices. She chose not to get up. They came to see her, standing again in the doorway. He had things to say, and a range of volumes to say them in, but the way Reba looked out of the bed shut him up. From that silence, the powerlines in the house began to rearrange.

The Girl with Earthworms in Her Mouth

By Chrissie Glazebrook

I keep it on the bookcase within reach, the shiny object, the
only memento I have of Mary. I stroke it like Aladdin's lamp and
wonder how differently things might have turned out. It glistens
unfeasibly, like something unearthly, some undiscovered material
from another planet. Mary worked hard for it; she earned it and
she gave it to me.

I was fourteen when we met. I'd been sent to London to stay with
Aunt Ivory because my mother could no longer look after me.
Mum had been ill for as long as I could remember; she crept around
the house like a ghost, shuffling in her slippers, clutching at the
banisters, puffing and wheezing. Now her organs had packed up,
I overheard Dad telling Aunt Ivory. I imagined musical instruments,
encased in wood, with stops marked *Celestina* and *Vox Humana*, that
had run out of steam and simply given up playing, squeaking
hoarsely to a stop. That was pretty much how it went.

Aunt Ivory was in domestic service in a house in London. To me,
an ignorant, unworldly lass from the North East, this sounded far
away and impossibly glamorous. True, it was a fair distance from our
two-up two-down terrace in Newcastle, but it turned out that there
was no glamour, just seediness and drudgery, so I was only half right.
She worked in a commercial hotel in Highgate, more what you'd call
a boarding house, catering mainly for travelling salesmen, defeated,
hopeless men, who sold household items door-to-door out of battered
suitcases. Aunt Ivory's room was on the top floor, up a winding flight
of stairs covered in threadbare carpet. She rose at dawn and set fires
in the grates before frying meagre breakfasts of eggs and streaky
bacon. Cholesterol hadn't yet been invented.

Some months later my mother died, followed not long after by my
dad. I was an orphan, cast adrift in a cruel, uncaring world. Jesus,
I thought, my evil aunt will send me up chimneys, or hire me out to
strangers for who-knows-what purpose, or throw me on to the cold
London streets where I would die of starvation in a gutter, to be
feasted on by rats and have my eyes pecked out by crows. Such
melodrama! But Aunt Ivory, despite her poverty, her Christian work

ethic and premature worn-outness, loved me and took me in to live with her in the boarding house.

She sent me to a Catholic school of unbearable strictness, where starchy old nuns taught us guilt, praying for lepers, and how to keep our hands occupied and out of our knickers. This is where I met Mary O'Brien, a pudgy flame-haired girl who wore National Health specs. She didn't belong to any particular set; she was neither liked nor disliked, and I can't say I noticed her until the day I found her with earthworms wriggling inside her mouth. A gang of girls had gathered round her, some ooh-ing and aah-ing at her courage, others gagging, repulsed. The ground was cold, she explained, so she was keeping the little darlings warm for a while. I didn't fall for this. We'd been learning in biology about earthworms – *lumbricus terrestris* and longworms – *allolobophora longa* – and she'd done it for a dare, I suspect, but nevertheless she went up in my estimation and we fell into a kind of friendship, chumming up at playtime, helping each other with homework, sniggering at the nuns behind our hands. One day she invited me to her house for tea.

Mary's home life was as far removed from Aunt Ivory's near-squalor as it was possible to imagine. The O'Brien family lived in an Irish enclave in Hampstead, where her father was some kind of fat cat. Despite this, their lives were characterised by a volatility which was foreign to me, unsettling in its noise and unpredictability.

The first time I went to visit, I almost turned tail and ran home. The size of the house was impressive and I shrank into myself, intimidated. The road was lined with trees, so unlike the grim street where Aunt Ivory and I lived. But to my horror, as I stood in the porch with my finger hovering over the doorbell, I could hear angry noises inside. Yelling, they were yelling at each other, although I couldn't make out the words. They were arguing loudly, shamelessly, as if they didn't care who could hear them. I hung back, mortified, stung with embarrassment. It was as bad as catching your parents having sexual intercourse. I later discovered that hollering was what passed for normal in the O'Brien household.

Eventually the door opened, revealing a tall, good-looking young man, whom I surmised from Mary's description to be Dion, her big brother. Despite his movie-star appearance, she reckoned he was a terrible bully, a hair-puller and shoulder-dislocator, though that could have been a lie to put me off. He was the kind of bloke that young girls had crushes on. He looked me up and down, with the kind of warmth reserved for someone selling clothes pegs or lucky heather.

'Stick! Stick, come on in.' Stick was Mary's pet name for me, on account of my thinness. She appeared in the doorway wearing dungarees and a check shirt like someone who'd turned up to hose the drains. She bustled in front of Dion, snarling, 'Shift, ya lummox', grabbed my arm and yanked me into the house.

If I'd thought it was posh from the outside, it was like a palace inside. The kitchen surfaces gleamed, the hall carpet looked brand new and everywhere smelt of furniture polish. Mrs O'Brien was writing a letter at a roll-top desk. She was a striking woman with flashing eyes and she looked exotic, dressed for going out, her hair in a chignon. I pictured Aunt Ivory with her harassed expression, her reddened hands and the wrap-around pinny that she wore constantly, and my face glowed with working class shame. This was how *I* wanted to live; in a big shiny house in an avenue, a place that stank of beeswax and money, somewhere with a garden where I could play out, where I'd be proud to invite friends round. I hated being poor and an orphan, feeling like a charity case.

Mary and I played in the garden, which seemed almost as big as a public park, charging around on bicycles, rocketing on the swings, climbing trees, squealing and shouting, until Mrs O'Brien called us in and sent us to wash in a bathroom the size of Hyde Park. Mary put on clean clothes and we went into the dining room and sat at a round table covered with a gleaming white cloth. My insecurities returned. I felt like a stray, a foundling, a street urchin, in my grubby second-hand dress and school sandals. Poverty hung around me like cheap scent, but the O'Briens treated me with civility and pretended not to notice.

Mary sat next to me, Dion opposite, and Mary's mother took the chair nearest to the kitchen. Mr O'Brien, they said, was in India, and I wondered what kind of person took his holidays in India, rather than at Butlins. I imagined him barefoot in a loincloth, rounding up wild elephants for a circus. I couldn't have been more wrong. He was, in fact, a rather portly income tax consultant who earned shed-loads of money.

This was the first time I heard the word 'casserole'. Mrs O'Brien served up stew and called it by a fancy name. Not stew ladled out of the pot into a chipped enamel dish, as Aunt Ivory would have done, but on a white plate with a bread roll and a pat of butter by the side, which I left untouched as I wasn't sure how to eat it. Along with the stew – the *casserole* – we each had three dumplings, dainty things moulded into little balls and speckled with herbs. I ate slowly in tiny nibbles, fearful of choking on a morsel of meat or gravy coming down my nose. The O'Briens waited politely for me to finish. I wanted to die. Then something flew across the table in front of me; a chunk of bread. And then another, and another. The posh people had started a food fight! This was something for which I had no terms of reference. I froze in my seat as a flying dumpling lodged in my hair. Mrs O'Brien joined in, tearing chunks of bread and lobbing them at her son or daughter, giggling with delight when they successfully hit their target. Alarming as it was, I discovered later that this misbehaviour was normal for the O'Briens – a food fight was their way of rounding off a meal.

Music, too, was a constant in their lives. They had a huge collection of vinyl and there was always a record spinning on the radiogram. It was a kind of music I was unfamiliar with; jazz was its name, and it sounded to me as though each musician was playing a different tune. Mary and her dad had a special game. He'd drum out a rhythm on her hand with his fingers and she'd say, *Satin Doll* or *Saint Louis Blues*. *Like Name That Tune* in Braille.

When she was sixteen, Mary had a radical change of image. Out went the glasses, replaced by contact lenses. The red hair was streaked with blonde highlights and backcombed into a beehive. She joined a girl group who wore sequins and sang in clubs. It was the beginning of her career in music and I could have died from envy.

Meanwhile, I'd developed into a tearaway, a teenage rebel, and was going out with Vic Neville, who dressed as a Teddy boy and carried a flick-knife. He was wild and colourful and dangerous and, if truth be known, part of the attraction was that I hoped Mary would be jealous.

She wasn't. Not in the slightest. Especially when I fell pregnant. I was sent to a mother-and-baby home, where I scrubbed floors to earn my keep and gave up my baby for adoption at three weeks old. Vic Neville was serving time in a borstal. Things could have been worse, I suppose.

And they did get worse, because after Vic, an unrepentant thug and the last Teddy boy in London, was released, we decided – for no reason that made sense – to get married. Aunt Ivory was beside herself. I had turned out to be a bad lot who went out jiving until all hours and had latched on to a thoroughly nasty piece of work.

Mary did her best to talk me out of it but my mind was made up: I was set on a steady course of self-destruction. I couldn't listen to her anyway. By this time she was singing in a group with her brother Dion and his friend. They'd changed their names, and they had a record contract. They were professionals. They were on the way up.

Quite out of the blue one evening, Mary rang me. She was in New York. Things were going well for her; she'd gone solo and was considered a big deal.

'How did you get my number?' That was how I greeted her. She called me from thousands of miles away and that's what I said.

'Never mind that,' said Mary, and her voice tore me up inside. 'You've been on my mind lately. I need to know how you're doing.'

How could I tell her I was miserable as hell, that Vic beat the crap out of me every Friday night, that I had an uncontrollable, impossible-to-love son?

'I'm good,' I assured her. 'Don't you worry about me, Mary. I'm doing fine. It's just a heck of a surprise to hear from you. You such a big star and all.'

There was a pause. I wondered how much this call was costing her. 'I'm in London next week,' she said. 'Why don't we get together, for old times' sake?'

Without thinking I said yes, and then a million worries flashed through my mind. How would I get away? What excuse would I use? What could I possibly wear? Suddenly I felt poor and haggard and wretched.

Aunt Ivory agreed to be my excuse, and my babysitter, for the evening. I swore her to secrecy and promised to be back, like Cinderella, by midnight. I can't say I looked like a million dollars, but my trouser-suit brushed up well.

My bony knees clacked together as I approached Mary in the hotel lounge. She was surrounded by her entourage and a scattering of well-known names, faces I'd seen on television, in magazines, even in movies. She was wearing her stage outfit, or something similar, a long cream dress cut in an Empire-line style. Her hair was completely blonde, professionally bouffed, and her eyes were almost hidden behind make-up. She looked every inch the star, yet she stood and came towards me, encircling me in a tight embrace.

'Stick,' she breathed, 'my darling Stick', and planted a showbiz kiss on my cheek.

'Mary,' I said, wondering how long it had been since anyone had called her that.

For the first time in my life I drank champagne and swallowed oysters. We were both a little drunk, Mary and I, when we made our way to her suite. The party continued. You would be amazed at the household names who were there, dancing, drinking, getting into some serious clinches and lip action. You would be amazed. I was stupefied, starstruck and gobsmacked.

Eventually the guests drifted away. Mary and I were alone and the air was electric, crackling, zinging with hormones and a strange, sinful attraction. I spent the night in her arms, the two of us like children in a huge mahogany bed. For a few hours her stardom ceased to daunt me and again we were convent girls, laughing ourselves stupid about the day she held earthworms in her mouth, the flying dumplings, the crush I'd had on her brother.

'Come with me,' she said, gazing earnestly into my eyes. 'Leave this tragedy you call your life. Be my – what shall we call it? – my *companion*.'

Of course I was tempted. Who wouldn't be? But the call of duty rang loud in my ears. My duty to the wife-beater Vic; to the selfish, wilful son; to the cockroach-infested flat I called home; to my working class roots.

'I'm not asking you to commit yourself. I know you can't guarantee anything. You're my oldest friend, Stick. I need you with me, by my side. If you find it's not for you, fine, you can leave. But please, baby, give it a try.'

Those were her words, but still I refused. I fled from the building as if the hounds of hell were at my heels. Returning half a day late to Aunt Ivory's, I flung myself on her bed and sobbed relentlessly before gathering up my ungrateful son and going home to prepare myself for Vic's fist. Mary's name was never again mentioned in our house.

I saw her funeral on the television. Star-studded, the reporter called it. Mary had developed cancer. She'd been presented with an OBE in hospital a month before she died. I felt desolate, a coward and a traitor. She had offered me the hand of true friendship and I had refused, ungraciously and ungratefully.

Some time later, after her lawyers had tracked me down, I received a gift from Mary. It sits here today, within reach, and I touch it often, remembering her, and the tears flow. It is a platinum disc and it bears her message: *You don't have to say you love me*, she sings, and I remember the girl with earthworms in her mouth.

Born 29 April 1939. Died 2 March 1999.
Born Mary Isobel Catherine Bernadette O'Brien. Died Dusty Springfield.

Bound

*This collection of stories was originally published as an
art book called* Bound (2004) *for which writers were
commissioned to create stories based in or inspired by
County Durham and Sunderland. To follow the stories,
readers had to construct each page. By the end of
the book, the pages had created a colourful rainbow sculpture.*

*We are including those stories in this book so that readers
can experience them in a more traditinal format. The book
also included essays by the writers which focussed on the
personal inspirations for their stories and their creative processes.*

Joyful Lagers of the World

By Charles Fernyhough

For a hundred years they'd been pumping the beer out of Sunderland, into the veins of tea-time drinkers and big-screen sports watchers from the eastern coalfields right up into the dale. Now the brewery had gone bust, the pubs were being sold off, and the last thing the administrators wanted to think about was the public health benefits of the brew that was Netherdale's Special Cask. Carl reckoned he'd done fifteen thousand pints of the stuff since he and Annie had been married. Little Georgie Milburn could put away thirty in a session. After a Saturday night shut-in there was more Special Cask in their bloodstreams than there was blood. He thought of those pale folk in Bishop Auckland General who had their plasma fed to them through a needle, how the smallest deviation from the correct mixture could send doctors running. Up here, where it snowed in June and the Top House was the only source of live entertainment, the supply of Special Cask was a life-support system. They'd just stopped brewing it. It was going to be a difficult winter.

'If Sportsman Leisure buy it, they'll be pushing their World of Beer export lagers.'

'You won't catch me drinking girls' beer,' Little Georgie said, seizing a new pint in his considerable fist.

'They're taking a risk,' Eric Alderson said. 'You'll remember that time they changed the brew up at Alston.'

They did remember, as it was only twenty years ago. Eric had spent most of that time on his stool at the end of the Top House's bar, next to a time-bleached stuffed badger that was being raffled for some long-forgotten charity. The cleaners had learned to hoover around him. Every so often he went home to the house next to Carl's and put the TV on in protest. Twenty years ago Eric had taken early retirement from his supervisor's job at Environment and Highways. On wintry days he still sometimes turned up to the pub in a council snow plough.

'My brother-in-law, Dennis, was living up there. He was a cheerful bugger, never left the house without a smile on his face. They started buying in this new malt from Canada. Never told Dennis. Never asked him whether he might react badly to a change in the water. After a few sessions on this new Canadian malt, Dennis starts feeling depressed. This man had never felt depressed in his life. Now he couldn't get out of bed in the morning. It was the malt. They'd changed the bloody beer. They do that down here and there'll be civil unrest.'

'They'll just shut the place down,' Tommy Hart said. 'They'll look at what this place is taking and say, too bad, not viable in today's harsh business climate.'

The Netherdale's logo shouted its protest from every ashtray on the bar.

'May as well shut the whole bloody village down,' the old fellow in the corner said. 'Finish what they didn't finish with the post office.'

'Not if we sort it ourselves,' Carl said out loud.

They looked at their drinking companion. Carl smoothed his cheek nervously with the back of his knuckled hand and straightened on his stool.

'It's not rocket science to get a brew going. You can go down to Morrisons and buy the gear.'

'Homebrew?' Eric laughed, clapping Georgie in the space where his shoulder-blades should have been. 'How's this one going to survive on the output of a cottage industry?'

'You can get European money,' Carl said. 'You set up a village cooperative.'

He was wondering where in their house he could fit a six-gallon tub. There'd be space in the rain-room if he shifted Annie's college files.

'It was the impurities,' Eric said. 'The esters and phenols and muck like that. That's what did for Dennis.'

'So you make it without impurities,' Carl replied. 'You make it with different impurities. Ones that make you feel good.'

'What are you talking about?' Tommy Hart said, skinning the plastic off a Hamlet.

Carl was trying to remember what Annie recommended to her bruised and torn first-time mothers.

'I'm saying you can put what you want in beer. I don't know. I'm just thinking.'

'Well, do it quietly,' Georgie said, dunking his upper lip into number 13.

The TV went on in the far corner, signalling a change-over of sessions. Within minutes the tea-time crowd had started to drift away. Through the bay window at the front of the pub, the winter afternoon was taking its time in dying. Walking back drunk in daylight would be a blow to Carl's self-esteem. But Annie would be home, wanting him to bath the bairn so that she could get the tea on.

'You'll have one more with me,' Eric told him, 'and then you can take me home before I forget where I live. Two for the road, please, Judith.'

The door swung open and Alan Kirby blew in with a freezer pack of lamb in a sports bag.

'Jesus Christ,' Eric said. 'Make that three.'

The house was dark. There was an empty baked bean can on the side, overturned in a skid of red sauce. Carl unlocked the door into the rain-room and stared at the dark, mildewed emptiness. It was an inauspicious starting point for a revolution in brewing. There were some greening plastic chairs he would sit on in the afternoons and resolutely face north. Some men had their garden sheds; Carl had his weather-permeable lean-to.

Annie and the bairn were watching *Please God Make Me Famous* in the sitting room.

'Where's your vadge tea?' he asked her.

'Pardon?' Annie mumbled into the soft nape of the bairn.

'The stuff you tell the mothers to drink. Ripen up the vagina.'

'The *cervix*.' She looked up, frowning. 'Raspberry leaf. In the green tin, next to the camomile.'

He set off, sweeping the bean can into the bin as he passed by.

'By the way,' she called after him, 'you haven't got a cervix...'

The kitchen cupboards were all at knee-level. He had to squat down on the cold flagstones to find the green tin. He lifted the lid and sniffed at its contents. It smelled no more soft-fruity than the flagstones. Eric's dog was staving off death behind the connecting wall. A bitter north-westerly was battering the glass sides of the rain-room. One of these days a gust was going to pick up these three white terraces and make off with them under its arm.

He got up, poked the PC on and watched Windows 1966 drag itself up into view. With each clunking sub-routine it was offering him a get-out clause: *press ESC to terminate*. Not even the computer was sure if it could get through this. When the desktop had finally built itself he double-clicked on his ancient browser and stared dully into the eyes of a naked woman draped over the bonnet of a classic truck. He googled **happiness beer** and watched his old modem tumble its red LEDs. There was talk of them sending broadband up the dale on the back of a huge airship, just like there was talk of them restoring the railway line and doing something with the Eastgate cement plant. For now, the twenty-first century was keeping to the other side of the Pennines, stopping in the Lakes for lunch before heading on to tourist-brochure Scotland. The only growth industry here was transport: moving stuff out of Durham as quickly as possible. The entrepreneurs were men who could magic things away. Carl's boss, Michael Thompson, had made himself a fortune hauling the topsoil out of the old Banks site and down the A68, trundling back at nightfall with the carrion of North Yorkshire. A worrying haze had come down that spring, the valley athrob with the rumble of wagons full of soil and diseased cattle. Carl was doing Sundays, bank holidays, staying in his cab while bio-suited workers loaded and unloaded, double-time, overtime, the whole crazy scam kept afloat by the panicked generosity of the taxpayer. When sanity returned it was to a world devoid of domesticated animals, hillsides whose lush pasture grew unchecked, stores of baled-up hay that couldn't be given away. When the farmers started restocking there was livestock work again, but half of them had taken their compo and bought themselves buy-to-lets in pretty villages in Cumbria. There wasn't the appetite for sheep any more, and so there weren't any sheep that needed moving. Michael Thompson was expanding in the Baltic region. The wagons on the A68 dwindled to a trickle, and Carl wasn't driving any of them.

The search engine had returned the usual half a million matches. Carl seized the grubby beige mouse and followed a link to a Belgian site which seemed to have scientific credentials. He squinted and ducked in closer. Somehow, when he'd had a few drinks, he didn't need his reading glasses. He learned that female hop-pickers were, before the introduction of automated harvesting techniques, notorious for suffering disturbances to their menstrual cycles. The presence of phyto-oestrogens in the hops conned the body into believing it was pregnant. The hop plant (*Humulus lupulus*) was a member of the family Cannabinaceae, to which hemp, or cannabis, also belonged. Carl sucked in a thin breath at the news. The next link in the list was offering aromatherapy products for sale through a secure website. A flurry of pop-ups made the screen freeze. Carl switched the machine off at the wall and went up the dark stairs, where he found the bathroom filled with the sweet, recent humidity of Annie. In the medicine cabinet was a tiny amber pill-bottle:

Arnica montana 6c
Homeopathic potency in 110 mg

He twisted off the safety cap and sniffed something sherbety, something floral. He tipped two of the sugary dots into his palm and swallowed them dry. Replacing the bottle, he was detained by the sight of a slim cardboard packet. He took it down and shook it, heard its voluptuous rattle. It had been there for years, a souvenir from a sunless, blank-faced holiday that Annie had never quite come back from. She'd gone along with the pills for a month or so and then given them up, shrugging on a determined bluffness, a smile that showed her embarrassment at all this attention to her sanity. He tried to think which of the doctors had prescribed them to her. A couple of years on, they all blurred into one clean-shaven consultant, who scribbled things on a pad and told them not to blame themselves. To start with, Carl had thought this was a drug to stop Annie miscarrying. So many fishy ghosts pushing up through the threadbare turf of their garden, so many little Mallorys who didn't make it to term. It was Mass that had got her through, the bells and smells, the whole comforting rigmarole of the weekly trip to St Mary's in Sunderland. The pills had stayed in the medicine cabinet and had mostly stayed out of their conversation. Carl still used them occasionally to round off a perfect session at the Top House. Now he was curious about the expiry date. It was six months ago.

He found himself staring at a single phrase on the side of the packet:

Selective Serotonin Reuptake Inhibitor

He put the packet back and went into the bedroom, feeling something stirring under the threshold of awareness, the faint swoon of connections being made. In an old cassette case in his socks drawer he found a broken-necked home-made cigarette that had been there since before the bairn was born. Its scruffy threads were tangled with black pleasure. He lay back on the bed and lit the spliff off an aromatherapy candle, which was effulgently spreading inner harmony from the bedside table. The TV soundtrack was lifting through the floorboards. He sucked air through the fragile paper and felt the first cool THC rush, the brother of hop, stir into his boozy bloodstream. Cannabinoid spoke unto cannabinoid. He fell asleep to the sounds of humiliation.

'Aromatherapy,' Carl said, lifting Morrisons bags out of the Hyundai's boot. 'The use of natural oils and extracts to promote personal health and well-being. I've read up on it. You use different hop-oil fractions at the end of the boiling to modify the aroma of the brew.'

'You want to make aromatherapy beer,' Eric said. 'In your bloody outhouse.'

They went in through the back door. Carl's new six-gallon tub was standing like a political statement on the kitchen table. There was a parcel from the mail-order company containing bottle caps and a hydrometer. Carl peeled off the bar-code sticker and carried the tub through into the rain-room. He could hear the bairn chuntering upstairs, Annie's footsteps creaking on the floorboards. Eric followed him into the rain-room, lugging a wine carrier full of special-offer real ales. He sat down on one of the plastic chairs and started reading in a disrespectful mock-Yorkshire accent from one of the beer bottles.

'For twenty years the small village of Shitbottle in Wharfedale has been the home of the Perfect Pig Brewery. Our glorious founder set the brewery up with the help of a bank overdraft and a derelict industrial premises. The mash room is the old...'

'Small village,' Carl observed. 'Derelict industrial premises.'

'Which you haven't got,' Eric said.

'Look around. Incline your eyes to the bloody hills. There's no shortage of dereliction.'

Eric raised a newly-filled pint glass to his lips and grimaced at the initial attack of Perfect Pig's Gruntbuster Ale.

'You need water,' Eric said, wiping away a bitter moustache. 'You need space for a bloody great big mash tun. You need power and access and room for conditioning. Can't just put the bugger up in your garden.'

Carl looked out over the slopes of their sub-valley. 'Begg's Mill,' he said, nodding a direction. 'Over that rise just there. No more than a mile from here. There's a burn. That water comes straight down from the top.'

Eric shook his head. 'Begg's is on the sheik's land. The whole job's preserved for grouse shooting. And there's not even a dirt track to get you up there.'

Annie came down the stairs into the sitting room. She was dressed for work, and her pale eyelashes had the darkish cling of something cosmetic. Her fair hair was up in a black-rooted bun. She caught sight of the Morrisons bags stacked up on the kitchen floor and noticed that they didn't contain food.

'Are yous two setting the world to rights?' she said, 'Or are you actually planning something dangerous?'

Eric looked at his watch, showing the traditional fear of drinking-partners' wives. He spoke of the imminent opening of the Top House, and a horse that was running at Towcester.

Carl was locked in contemplation of his wife. 'I said I'd look after the bairn this afternoon.'

'There's snow forecast,' Annie said mysteriously.

'There's always snow forecast. We're halfway up the Pennines.'

Annie saw the empty beer bottles. 'Have yous been drinking?'

'We're not talking about light machinery,' Carl said. 'I can operate a baby after two pints.'

'Mind, you'll need financing,' Eric said, getting up to go. 'You don't know the first thing about brewing. You'll have to go and beg for some money. Talk to our neighbour Mr Kaprowicz. He might find a couple of thousand to get you started.'

'If he gets a couple of thousand for anything,' Annie said, 'it'll go on building two new bedrooms for this place.'

Carl did not want to discuss Annie's extension, not now or ever. He went upstairs and found Mallory chewing on the lip of her cot. He lifted her soft, spring-loaded body and stared into her pushed-up cheeks. He told her that it began here, this afternoon; that this was the day he took the wrapper off his life. He lifted her higher and let her suck on the tip of his nose, which made her giggle. She was his little confessor, his priest in pink gingham. She was the proof that it could happen. He held her close and felt her turtle weight snuffling at his neck, breathing hotly into his ear. Then, his heart calmed by the small sounds that still seeped out from her, he started rooting in the wardrobe for her snowsuit.

Dark shapes fled across the hillside, the shadows of fast-moving clouds. Under Carl's boots, dead root-growths, bleached white like animal bones, crunched with a sound like eggshells. He feared for ground-nesting birds, but there were no footpaths through this forest of heather. The baby carrier on his back dug its padded wings into his sides. He could reach back and squeeze Mallory's unshoed feet through the toes of her snowsuit. If he craned his neck right round, he could just catch a suspicion of her black eyes under her fleecy hood. She was awake. Her body had surrendered all muscle-tone, but her seven-month-old brain was open for education.

'They laughed at the Beatles, pet,' Carl said. 'They laugh at all the millionaires.'

Miles to the east, the A68 threaded down from Northumberland, twinkling with the cabs of working drivers. The land underfoot was still damp with old snow. Streams of meltwater were embedded in the hillside, running silently through culverts of grass, roofed by dry skins of ice. Carl struggled on against the slope. Gradually the land levelled out and he could see the far inclines of the dale, contours of ungrassed brown that looked haphazardly denuded, like restless holiday sleepers that had shucked off their bedclothes. A flock of lapwings dipped and scattered sideways. Through the lenses of his sunglasses, the clouds appeared orange-pink.

'There,' he told the bairn. 'Begg's Mill.'

What he and Mallory were looking at was a sandstone building, roofed with fragments of ash-grey timber, with a couple of barn-sized outhouses which Carl, in the idealism of forethought, had set aside for maltings. A collapsed iron footbridge ran into deep burn-water. The cost of the thing, the sheer extent of the renovation project, pushed his heart into a blissful cruise. Happiness was an ephemeral gift, bestowed at random by a disorganised God. You could take it in a pill or you could work for it by trying to shift the furniture of life. It was the same light-headed feeling. Whether you'd earned it or not, it was the same deep-burning glow.

He stopped, rethinking thoughts. You could take it in a pill. The pills were in their medicine cabinet. Whatever you had in a pill, you could put into beer.

The wind muttered in his ears. Clouds scudded over the summit of the hill, almost head-high to a man.

'Anti-depressant lager,' the millionaire Kaprowicz was saying. 'You want to make anti-depressant lager.'

'Ale,' Carl corrected him. 'It's all in the structure of the hop-oil fractions. The lager process destroys all the complex molecules. It has to be a real ale.'

'But I don't like real ale. I like lager.'

The dark-skinned beauty on his arm laughed. She liked whatever the millionaire liked.

'You're modifying the hops, right?' Carl explained. 'So they're producing an SSRI.'

'Modifying?' The millionaire's *EastEnders* accent seemed to ring out through the crowded pub. 'Like, genetically?'

Carl nodded coolly. 'I found a website. Big American biotechnology company. They'll do it all for you.'

'So what's this SSR-wotsit?' Mr Kaprowicz said.

'Selective serotonin reuptake inhibitor. It's what Prozac's a one of.'

'They're genetically modifying hops to make Prozac?'

'No.' Carl shook his head. 'They're genetically modifying them to make them resistant to pesticides. *We're* going to make Prozac. Real ale with the added smile factor.'

'You can't just grow Prozac on trees,' Tommy Hart said. 'The big corporations would have done it by now.'

'Aye,' Eric agreed. 'Aromatherapy's one thing. But now you're stretching my imagination a bit too bloody far.'

Carl started to regret having this conversation in public. 'Alcohol's a depressant, right? That's why Dennis gets miserable after he tries the Canadian malt. But you can balance out the depressant by putting other stuff in. There's more to beer than alcohol.'

'More's the pity,' Georgie Milburn said.

The millionaire caught sight of someone he knew. 'So how much will this little adventure cost you?'

'I need to renovate Begg's Mill and equip it as a brewery. You can

buy in all the coppers and mash tuns and everything second-hand.
There's enough small breweries that have gone to the wall.'

Eric was listening in dismay. 'That's his point, Carl. They've all
gone to the bloody wall.'

'So you're not going to lend me the money?' Carl asked Mr
Kaprowicz.

'You show me the business plan. You show me the research that
says this is all possible. And then,' the millionaire sniggered and
turned to the dusky starlet at his side, 'I'll put it to the board.'

Carl glanced around nervously. The pub was full of strange
goggle-eyed teenagers who looked like they'd never seen sunlight. He
had the bizarre feeling of having been kept down a year at school.

'You made money, Mr Kaprowicz. You must have taken a risk
or two.'

'I made money buying up failing businesses and setting them
straight. Not by starting up the failures in the first place. There's
money in lager. Lifestyle choices, themed entertainment venues.
There's no money in real ale.'

'I told you. You can't genetically modify lager.'

'You see, you have to have a brand.' The millionaire was warming
to his theme. 'You need a profile, recognition, visibility. Lagers of the
World. Sportsman Leisure's World of Beer.' He supped appreciatively
at his tall pale pint. 'Sportsman have got that just right.'

'Carl?' the bar girl shouted. 'Is there anyone here called Carl?'

Eric snatched the phone off her. 'You can learn some customers'
names if you're going to stop there behind them sticks.'

'Aye,' Alan Kirby slurred. 'That lad there's your bloody family.'

Carl took the receiver. It felt strangely unweighted, abraded by
thousands of bar-side excuses and bookmaking calls. It was Annie,
saying that her home confinement was three centimetres dilated.

'I'll just finish this pint,' Carl mumbled, witnessing the arrival of
two more.

'You will not,' Annie said. 'You're coming home to look after
Mallory so I can go to work. She feels hot. I've given her a dose of
Calpol but you'll need to check her temperature every two hours.'

Carl gulped determinedly at the endangered ale, stubbed out his
cigar and went coatless into the night. He passed the Methodist
chapel and a line of rain-stained council houses, then cut across the

field that looked over the millionaire Kaprowicz's mansion, set in its own gated and surveillanced valley, its computer-controlled lighting system giving it a semblance of human occupancy. He thought of Eric's National Service .22 rifle, the one he kept behind the bedroom door for when the burglars came for his jewels, and wondered if he'd be able to shoot out a window from this distance. As the lane unfurled its spectral darknesses he began to feel the chill of the January night, sense the chemical scent of snow. The lights were on in Number Two. Annie and the bairn were waiting for him in the sitting room.

'Teeth,' Carl murmured, diagnosing the teary soreness of Mallory's cheeks. 'Has she had the gel?'

Annie shook her head. 'Are you sure you're all right to look after her?'

He nodded, understanding. Sometimes it was like this: you saw a raw, anticipated grief in her eyes as she prepared to hand the bairn over, a sense that even this vigorous infant was contingent, a consolation prize that could be taken back at any moment. Until she'd clipped on the brisk cheerfulness of the midwife, it was as though she believed there was still some debt they had to pay, for those little sisters and brothers who hadn't pushed through. He watched her hurry into her coat, and had the usual feeling that he didn't deserve her.

'This is a third baby, pet,' she said. 'They come out quickly. And they're all the way up at Cowshill.'

'Mind the speed cameras,' Carl called after her. 'Mind the brave guardians of the empty road.'

He washed his hands at the kitchen sink and fingertipped a pearl of teething gel onto Mallory's gums. The bairn's sharp new teeth bit down hard on his finger. He withdrew it and checked it for damage, then felt her forehead. His frozen hands made the baby complain more. He hugged her close and jigged despondently around the room with her, then with one hand unlocked the door to the rain-room. His homebrew experiment was still standing there in its six-gallon tub, awaiting a test of its specific gravity. He had an urge to push it out into the yard, kick it over and let the whole piss-smelling disaster flood away. He was wasting his time. He couldn't save Special Cask for the world. He went back into the sitting room, sat down with Mallory on the leather settee and pointed the remote control at the fireplace. For a dizzy moment he couldn't understand what had gone wrong. Was he drunk, or was this just the rot that set in when you frittered your life away in front of daytime TV? He'd had five pints of Special Cask, possibly the last he would ever taste, but for once it wasn't the beer. This sickness in his soul was drug-resistant, untreatable; not even the pills in the medicine cabinet could lift him out of this. His only option was flight. Getting away from the place where he'd failed so spectacularly to operate the light machinery of his life.

He looked at Mallory. She was staring at the TV, cramming fingers into her mouth as if they were seafood delicacies. He looked out at the dark night in the window. When he lost his driving job he would go walking for hours, day or night, trusting nothing but the swish of grass against his boots, dreaming nothing beyond the view from the next rise. The pain was less when he was moving. When you got some height between yourself and the problem, you saw it like the hills saw it: distantly, greyly, a glimpse of human business that was instantly forgotten. It was hard to stay attached to things, up there under that draughty sky.

He saw the bairn's snowsuit hanging up by the door.

'Come on, pet. Mountain air's good for a fever.'

She complained a little when the snowsuit went on, but then let herself be slotted without fuss into the velcro'd cage of the baby carrier. He put a coat on and pulled her onto his back, then picked up his torch and went outside. The road was empty. A few flakes of snow had started to fall. He stood in the road under their one street lamp, listening for signs of life. A daggy sisterhood of sheep was staring aimlessly in the same direction. He climbed over the wall into the field and started to trudge up through the long grass. The beam of his torch was a brittle baton of light, conducting the stillness erratically. Halfway up the hill he stopped and looked back at the little settlement where a few lives, his included, clung to the hillside. This was not a place where dreams took hold. This was a place people retreated to when they had no dreams, where the best you could hope for was a life like your parents', shopping on a Friday for a weekend that never came. It was a place where life shrank to fit people's expectations of it, where anyone who wanted to shift the furniture had to expect to be mocked mercilessly. He wanted to make his own beer. It wasn't a call for revolution.

'If you ever have an idea, pet, keep it to yourself. That's what the millionaires do.'

There was no reply. He reached back and felt for Mallory's bare wrists under her gloves. She felt cold. He shrugged off the baby carrier and looked at her in the faint light coming up from the street lamp. Her eyes were open and she was staring past him, struck by some supernatural power now lost in the night sky. He shone the torch on her, panicking, then switched it off when she started to fuss. He reached in, unclipped the harness and pulled her out, feeling her arch backwards then bat at his chest as he pulled her close. She wasn't ill, just learning. But what was he teaching her? A bitter lesson in his own beardy, boozy language, a joke unsuitable for children. He followed her gaze up to the summit. The heather overtook the grass up there. A black cloud hung above them, shedding snow, but the rest of the sky had the clarity of deep space. He saw it reflected i n the tiny lights of his daughter's eyes, which were fixing him again, intrigued by his anger. Then he saw her beady indifference turn back to the horizon, carrying his dreams to a patch of space above a hillside, where a little star hung above Begg's Mill.

The Separation Wall

By Fadia Faqir

'The drop of rain maketh a hole in the stone, not by violence,
but by oft falling.'
Hugh Latimer

Durham, 2004

That cold autumnal night with clear skies was perfect for carrying
out my mission. When I hung a camping lantern on the metal hook,
left by the previous owner for a dainty flower basket, a faint sickly
light spread over the garden like disease. I tied a wire to the two pegs
I'd dug at either end of the high right fence, sprinkled some sand to
create a line then pulled the pegs out and began digging thin layers
following the line in the sand. The moist sand responded, unlike the
Baghdadi sand I'd left behind, which was baked dry by the hostile
sun. I pushed the shovel deep into the cold earth, pushed the handle
down, raising the dark soil which was full of broken pieces of clay
and bits of concrete up and up, then dropped them on the lawn. He
had to be buried instantly, but the dry sand resisted. The grave had to
be about two metres deep. The trench had to be thirty centimetres
deep to lay the foundations.

The sweet mint tea I made for myself earlier was tepid by now.
I had a sip and instantly I was back in our garden in Baghdad,
drinking tea with my mother and grandmother. Why did she call me
Khalid? Immortal? Me? The smell of dark fertile soil filled the
evening air and travelled beyond my garden to warn my English
neighbours that I was up to no good. When they heard that an Arab
had bought the house next door, they erected a fence two metres high
to protect themselves, but the brick wall I was building would be
even higher, and be solid and enduring. Although I sometimes
dreamt of inclusion, most of the time I wanted total privacy and
exclusion, I wanted safety. My life revolved around departures. Next
stop: Mind the gap.

Kalkelie, 2004
Looking at the evening sky I could hear the dogs barking and the slam of machinery. The sun was about to set, turning its backs on us mortals, captive here on this very earth. Once upon a time, the storage room was full of wheat, hay, barley, guava, jars of pickled olives, tins of olive oil, plum, peach and apple jam, their white flakes of almonds glinting through the clear glass jars. You would not expect less of the precious soil of Kalkelie, the fertile womb of Palestine, returning three-fold every seed thrown. The sick smell of damp and mould filled the empty room. The walls, which used to be white, turned grey as if in mourning.

It was summer time and the engagement season had begun, but the beats of the tabla were muffled this year and no one had any energy to ululate. Grief, sister, took it out of you. The thick old walls blocked off the heat of the sun, leaving the storage room cold and eerie as if haunted by ghosts. I untied my headscarf, took off my black dress, my white bloomers, cotton slip, and plastic slippers, then stood in the middle of the room shivering. I ran my fingers over my stomach, stretched into age by the five pregnancies I had had. You would think that giving birth to five sons is a good thing and that you would not end up alone in your old age. Well, think again.

My mother's good luck charm was in the Damascene wooden box my late husband had given me on our wedding day. The dark oak was carved then inlaid with silvers of mother of pearl. The red velvet lining always a surprise. My mother, God bless her soul, was called Halimeh; patient and mellow she was; like a full moon, she was; like a balm for your soul, she was. She used to carry a straw tray decked with food to the courtyard, calling our names one by one until finally she called mine, Huriya, virgin of paradise. They are all dead now, except me.

Magna, AD 197-217
Alexander to Augustus, his son, many greetings! Every night I ask the Mother of gods, Ceres, dea Syria, who weighs life and laws in her balance, to protect you. Your father, Augustus the Hamii, is an archer in the Emperor's auxiliary army and will be stationed at the fortress of Magna, honoured guard of the Roman Empire's northern frontier.

A proud Roman citizen of twenty-three years, for which I left Antioch the valley of greenery on the Orontes River, heading towards the unknown. I should go. It was my call and binding duty. I slung my bow over my shoulder, and slid my iron sword in its leather scabbard. I travelled towards my destiny. The Roman generals recruited a legion of archers able to shoot arrows as far as the sanctuary of Zeus and beyond. The auxiliaries, who were lightly armed, and we the archers, were ordered to march first, followed by armed footmen and horsemen, while the carriages of commanders were at the very end of the column. We marched through the wilds of unknown countries, crossed rivers and seas until the centurion's voice spat out, 'Britannia.' We had arrived. I am safe.

Salutations to your mother, my brother and his children and all your loved ones!'
Deliver at Antioch to Augustus, from his father Alexander the Hamii.

Durham, 2004
There they were at the end of the horizon: the cathedral and castle, which I have read about so much since Durham Telecom offered me the job, constant reminders of my foreignness and insignificance. I got out of the train, dragging my heavy suitcase, which contained all my worldly belongings, behind me. In the dark corner at the back, where I had folded my underpants neatly and arranged them in a pile, it lies quietly, inside a wooden box, wrapped up in tissue paper and held into place with rubber bands. I could hear it throbbing sometimes.

I walked down North Road, dragging my dusty suitcase behind me. The screeching sound of the worn-out wheels announced my arrival in this town. Passers-by fixed me with their accusing gaze. I had dark hair, eyes, skin, and wore a fine moustache just like my father's. Open heart surgery might show that even my lawless heart is black. Who knows? I walked like a criminal waiting to be convicted. If I kept my head down I might not be spotted inhaling their fresh air and taking up their space.

Then I saw her, walking in beauty down the street, the mother of all English roses, and suddenly my suitcase became lighter and the air cooler.

I dug the soil even harder as if looking for the source of my pain. It was so quiet I could hear my heart beating, but I was a man with a mission. I put the sand and cement in a large bucket, added some water then began mixing. When I poured the grey mortar into the trench it filled it lazily and the smell of fresh concrete filled the air. We had to bury him in the garden, where else? In the darkness I could see my grandmother's forehead gleaming with sweat while she struggled with the shovel. 'Let us hope that the neighbours are heavy sleepers.'

Kalkelie, 2004

When I touched the blue beads of the good luck charm, I started crying like a suckling without a mother. Naked, wrinkled, old and defeated, I stood in the middle of the storage room sobbing. My eldest son, Mohammad, went to America thirty years ago, and not a word, my sister, not a single word. Some say he got married to a beautiful American woman, from a grand clan, and was ashamed of his peasant family, and others say he was dropped in the Atlantic when the marine police approached the ship to look for illegals. Rumour has it that the Greek captain who dropped him in the sea was killed in Tangiers by the families of the other Moroccan immigrants, who were with him on the same boat, and who were also flung hurriedly into the sea. Khalil joined the resistance movement and then died a 'natural death' while being interrogated. Karim, the apple of my eye, my favourite son, who used to bring me dates whenever he came to visit, was shot by a sniper while walking home. Alcohol and smoking killed Fathi. As for Samir, my youngest, he went to a far away land to fight the communists, enemies of Islam, twenty years ago, and since then my eyes were never soothed with his sight.

In the black and white photo, which I kept in the box, my children looked happy standing there under the fig tree. My husband, who passed away in his sleep, was carrying Samir in his arms. My mother stood right next to me, holding Karim's hand. Framed by the veil her face looked round and radiant. Then suddenly an invisible hand cut the string that binds the rosary, and all the beads rolled down, each in a different direction, never to be held together again.

Magna, AD 197–217

'Before all I pray for your health. I myself am well, and make supplication for you before the gods. We arrived in the place of yew trees, the fort of Eboracum on the Ouse River, in good health on the moon day of the month of Aprilis, and were posted to Magna. I beg you then, son, look after your mother and do not worry about me; for I have come to a fine place. You probably never saw a yew tree in your life. It is thick and green with needle-shaped leaves with fine buds; it is poisonous to cattle and people plant it where they expect to be buried. One day my yew tree, which is neither of the East nor of the West, will be planted to mark my grave.

By now and with the judicious help of your tutor Alexus, you must be able to read and write Latin. Persevere, young Augustus, for your future will be much better than mine! The world holds no greater son than you. Please write me a letter about your welfare and that of your mother and of all your folk. Many salutations to you all and my brother and his children!'

Durham, 2004

My neighbours were polite but curt. Java, which I spoke very well, was worthless in such surroundings. Like a vast blue sea, language, history and culture stretched between us and turned us into little islands of solitude. 'Did you say Kaleed?' If I took the garbage out, I would feel their burning gaze on my back, and whenever I washed the car they would put away their gardening tools and hide indoors. I told my young colleague James, 'It was Neighbourhood Muslim Watch,' and he thought that I was serious and that there was such a scheme in Durham.

Getting permission to build this damned wall around my own garden was difficult: deeds, drawings, history of building, precise plans, neighbours' consent, and finally the council approval. If I had an army of space invaders I wouldn't have asked for permission; I would have terminated all my neighbours with laser guns. I began measuring my property very carefully. The fence at the back ate up four inches of my land and if I replaced it with a wall I would end up gaining up to three inches of my neighbour's land through straightening the curve. Not bad! A greater kingdom for King Khalid!

I began dreaming about building a brick wall around my garden so high that no one could see me or hear me.

When I was young my father used to watch me carefully for two reasons: he was afraid of me and what I could do and he was afraid of them and what they could do. The intelligence service was spying on him, so he spied on all of us and policed us. Fear in our house ran down the walls like nicotine. Whenever my mother hid the cat, slippers, belts and wooden stools in the cupboard of my bedroom and shushed me to silence I knew that my father was having one of his fits. After three hours we would come out of our hiding place and assess the damage. My grandmother would whisper, 'The dining table was broken. Not too bad this time. What Allah had given He had taken away.' My mother would start laughing, a sound somewhere between a titter and a sob.

Kalkelie, 2004

My mother, Halimeh, who was so patient and mellow, began to lose her patience and sight. She refused to leave Tira, where she had lived all of her life, although it had become a handful of deserted stone houses. Our house was one of the best in the village. It had high, round-arched windows and a flat roof, with a yard full of olive, orange and lemon trees. I used to chase the hens out of their barbed-wire cage and my mother used to chase them back, lock the padlock and then hide the key in the cloth pocket, where she used to hide money. Whenever I wanted to be near her I would stick my fingers inside her dress, pretending to look for that hidden pocket, but lingering above the generous breasts. She would hug me and shower me with kisses. 'Do you want a dose of kindness, Huriya?'

I begged her to come and live with me, and promised her that I would do anything, absolutely anything, if she blessed my house with her presence. She finally said, 'I will come to live with you on one condition. Soon, when I die, bury me in the courtyard of my house in Tira next to your father's grave, may Allah protect you.' I held her rough dark hand and said, 'I promise.'

She walked to the bedroom, took my father's black and white photo off the wall, wiped the dust with the end of her veil, then kissed his face. 'Mercy upon you, mate of my soul. Your sweet breath still fills this room.' She ran her hands on the bedcovers, embroidered by my grandmother, then the wardrobe, the bedside table, the mirror frame and, when she saw her reflection in the mirror, her chin began quivering. 'Get me a glass of water, bless you.'

When I came back I found her sitting at the end of the bed, her wedding chest was open and she was packing. She wrapped her summer and winter dresses, her ivory comb, her cotton drawers, her headscarves and her Ottoman milaya wrap in a bundle, then stood up.

We shut the windows and the doors and then secured the main gate with a padlock. I could see her new neighbours watching us through the metal bars of their windows. A final glance at her overgrown garden and empty courtyard, then balancing the bundle on her head, she said, 'Let's go.'

Magna, AD 197-217

'Before all I pray for your health. I myself am well, and make supplication for you before the gods. I am now stationed at the fort of Magna south of Hadrian's Wall and Vallum as part of the Cohors I Hamiorum. Our job is to guard the junction of Aesica and Camboglanna overlooking the Tipalt Gap and keep the Caledonian Picts out. It was impossible to introduce the barbarian Picts to the Roman way of life. Can you imagine a highlander wearing a toga and babbling on in Latin? The great Emperor Hadrian ordered the construction of the defensive wall to mark the northern limits of his empire using local labour to cart Roman stones, but although the locals worked hard they were not allowed to carve their names on the stones like the Roman quarrymen. So, my son, the barbarians built this wall to keep themselves out and separate themselves from the civilised Romans. Our job is to guard the wall, keep Rome's enemies out and stop the Caledonian terror. But the worshippers of Brigit were undeterred; they smeared themselves with blue paint and screeched like monkeys when approaching the dark ridges of Magna. They would throw their ropes and ladders to climb up and before they were close enough to throw their javelins, we would plant a Hamii arrow in their very heart.

We are soldiers and this is what great soldiers do.

Virgil puts me in a pensive mood. Standing here on the wall, looking beyond the end of the world, I sometimes wonder what the future holds. Will this wall, this great edifice, outlast us all or will it be dismantled by the same barbarian hands that built it? Will it endure under this western gloom or will it become irrelevant for humanity? Why? *Felix qui potuit rerum cognescere causas.*

Please write me a letter about your welfare and that of your mother and of all your folk. Many salutations to you all, my brother and his children!'

Durham, 2004

It was so cold that my breath froze, forming different shaped white clouds. The smoke signals were barely visible; they rose all the way up then evaporated, leaving nothing behind. I had laid the first layer of bricks, knocking each one gently into place, scooping off the excess mortar with my trowel then dropping it into the plastic bucket. The horizontal liquid in the spirit level indicated that the wall was even. I looked up to check if I were being watched. There was no one around except the king himself, me. The moon had disappeared finally, and a hushed silence descended on the neighbourhood like fog.

The plastic garden chairs were the cheapest in the market. Most of my salary went on the mortgage and monthly bills, and falling in love cost me dearly. I used to do my food shopping at Somerfield, but since I set my eyes on her I began buying the bread bun by bun when it was her shift at the checkout in Sainsbury's. It used to cost me twenty-seven pounds to buy all my rations for the week, but buying only two items at a time and driving to Sainsbury's five times a week added about a hundred odd pounds to my monthly expenditure. The plan was to expose her to my dark face as much as possible until it became familiar so that when I gathered some courage to approach her, she would not panic and call the manager.

Like a mole I worked frenziedly at night, burrowing holes. When the first metre of the wall was dry and solid I began laying more bricks. The garden was rectangular in shape and through straightening the lines and raising the dark brick wall it began to look and feel like a room. I was close to finishing so I decided to work all night if necessary and receive the new dawn in the glory of my new haven.

I wiped the sweat off my forehead with my sleeve, and sat down. Even my arm was trembling with exhaustion.

I had a funny feeling that I was being watched. Pairs of eyes flashed in the darkness: my neighbours? The police? Anti-terrorist Branch? Probably some FBI agents? The wall should make it really hard for anyone to see me while squatting on the lawn talking to myself, or even listening to Arabic songs.

Kalkelie, 2004

Towards the end of her life my mother began seeing her children floating around. 'They are back,' she announced, 'like threads or thin clouds inside my eyes. I could see them, feel their presence, and hear their voices summoning me to join them. It shan't be long now.' I took her to the storage room and despite her attempts to push me away I undressed her then washed her body with soap and water. 'See how your daughter treats me,' she said to the walls. Since she had moved in with me she would not let me wash her clothes so her long black dress had gotten really dirty and her white drawers had dark yellow stains running down them. I wrapped her in my father's woollen cloak and asked her to sit on the door step in the sun to get warm. I washed her clothes and hung them on the washing line to dry.

She sat there on the doorstep talking to the clouds, 'I told him that this defeat will be followed by many others, even more bitter in taste... he melted away that night like a grain of salt... they will kill us... the tar lined his lungs... white clouds of dust to build a new road... olive trees... why doesn't he listen to me?' She seemed distressed. Her left eye kept wandering away to one side and she kept rubbing her hands together. I hugged her, filling my nostrils with her smell. She was so thin. A bundle of bones replaced the robust woman who used to be my mother. I sat her down and gave her some warm milk with honey. When she finished drinking I helped her get dressed. Her hair was patchy and grey, her breasts almost touched her waistline and her mouth was slightly bent to the right as if she were about to smile. That night, when the moon was in the middle of the sky, clean as a baby and smelling of lilies, Arabian jasmine and olive oil, my mother departed.

Magna, AD 197-217

'I called you Augustus after the great Roman Emperor, who lived in modesty, a model leading citizen's life. Power did not corrupt him or stop him from taking heed or consulting the senate. He was the perfect democrat. When I left you, my son, there was little time for saying goodbye. I looked at your brown eyes, kissed your hands and left without a backward glance. I knew if I looked back I would have lost my nerve and would not have been able to pursue my journey; I knew in my heart that I might never see you again, and that our farewell was final. Since then I suffer from a permanent tightening of the chest and a mild cough. How did I come to be here? What evil or good powers were to blame for this? Who would put things right for me?

The inkwell has dried up and I have to lay down my nib for the night. Salutations, young Augustus!'

Durham, 2004

'*Maali shughul bilsuuq maryt ashuufak.*' I have no reason to go to the market place, but I pass by to have a glimpse of my beloved. Katy, who was probably nineteen or twenty, was tall with thin legs and arms. She had long arty fingers with small round nails always painted discreet pink. Her long blonde hair was neatly tied back with colourful bands. Whenever she looked at me with her amazing blue eyes, my heart would stop. Her radiance was so unbearable I used to lower my gaze and think of my father's finger. Everything she did made me feel stronger and weaker at the same time: the way she tilted her head to one side, the way she straightened the bank notes with her delicate fingers before she gave them back, the way she rubbed her forehead when she was unsure about the price of lemons. She looked so young and fragile that something in my inner being wanted to protect her.

When I finally gave her my card with the money, she smiled then lowered her gaze. She did not report me to the security guard as I expected. Then the waiting for that damned phone call began. Seven weeks came and went without a word although my mobile phone was hooked to my belt all the time. Nothing. Maybe she threw the card in the bin? Maybe she wanted to call me late at night when no one was listening? Maybe she was too afraid of my foreignness? I worked hard on convincing myself that she would never ever ring and after I succeeded the phone rang and it was her. She said that her mum would like to meet me on Sunday, and gave me their address. A bit quick, I thought, but after all I am a foreigner and had to be vetted carefully.

I would break her in gently. First I would introduce her to coffee with cardamom, then mint tea, then my Arabic CDs, then the photo of my family under the palm tree, then lamb stew. She would get excited and curious. I would be patient and take twice the time I spent getting to know my Iraqi sweetheart. As a computer engineer I wanted this relationship to function properly and had to do a realistic estimate of the time it would take to get intimate. My pragmatism told me that it would take at least nine weeks before I could kiss her. She would fall in love with me and in six months' time I might even ask for her hand in marriage.

Kalkelie, 2004

Slam. One morning, sister, I heard some explosions just past the valley, so I ran to have a look and there they were, blowing up rocks and clearing the land to build a fence. We were given no warning when the dynamite would explode, so you would be having your morning coffee with your neighbour and off it goes, splitting your head apart and throwing the cup out of your hand. Then they uprooted hundreds of olive trees, fifty of which were yours truly's, to clear the land. Slam.

I stood in the storage room still not knowing what to do next, so I performed my wash and ablutions. I poured some warm water over my head and lathered my hair with soap. I was losing so much hair and if you look carefully you would find my grey hair every-where, even in the bread I ate. When I pulled, a strand of hair came out in my hand. At this rate I would be bald soon and the beautiful thick braids my late husband used to praise would be no more. I rubbed the loofah with soap, creating lather, then scrubbed my legs and arms really hard until they turned red then poured some water over my head. No matter how hard I scrubbed, the pain and the noise lingered.

My legs were trembling so I sat on the straw chair and put my head between my knees as advised by the doctor of the town. Since his house was demolished last year you would find him in the middle of the market-place, sitting behind a small wooden table under a green parasol. He was given forty-five minutes to move before the bulldozers began flattening his house, so he hurriedly collected his photo albums, shoved his clothes into black bin liners and rescued as many medical tools as he could from his home surgery. He said there was nothing wrong with me 'except you get dizzy with exhaustion sometimes, so place your head between your knees or lie down until the spell passes'. 'Nothing wrong with you' was exactly what I did not want to hear. I wish he'd said you have cancer in every bone of your body, I wish he'd said your heart is about to stop, I wish he'd said you have blood on your brain and you will end up unconscious for the rest of your life. But he said there was nothing wrong with me, sister.

Magna, AD 197-217

'After serving on the wall for a month, doing both day and night shifts, I was granted the privilege of a day leave and a visit to the bath house at Vindolanda. We go to the public bath house to cleanse ourselves, relax our limbs and see our friends. As soon as you enter the tepidaria you can hear the grunts of men lifting weights and the slaps of massage on naked bodies. After anointing my body with olive oil, I sat down in the hot water next to Antony the Roman, which proved to be a big mistake. He had been eating fermented fish again and his halitosis filled the air. Although I had several fits of coughing, Mark, in his youthful impatience, went on ranting about a woman called Regina, who apparently fell for the charm of a Pict farmer, who used to cross the gate frequently to sell his produce. The commander stripped her of her Roman citizenship, ordered his soldiers to cut off her breasts, stitch them to her mouth, as if she were eating them, stick a long piece of metal all the way through her and hung her naked on the main road. They say that the commander wept and tore his hair all night.

There she was, naked and defenceless, dangling from a post outside in the parade ground. Regina looked so haunting in the sunset.

We normally inflict this on our enemies. We are soldiers. This is what we do.

How is your mother, the mistress of my soul?'

Durham, 2004

I wore my best suit, dabbed some aftershave on my chin, bought the largest bouquet of flowers and drove to their house. Their garden was in full bloom. The palms of my hands were so sweaty when I finally rang the bell.

When I knocked the last few bricks into place, my whole body was trembling. The spirit level was not even, so I had to hammer down the last two rows, shattering the mostly dry mortar. I sat down on the damp lawn, chiselling the mortar off the bricks. Eyes flashing everywhere! The two men, who sat smoking and drinking coffee in the blue Fiesta outside my house, were Special Branch. The police were following me wherever I went. They kept changing their car in order not to be noticed, but I knew that I was being watched constantly. They even got my neighbour to park their car for them and get out of it, then give them back the keys when I was not around. Whenever I picked up the phone I could hear the hissing of tapes being rewound.

I fitted the last brick into place. Two police officers came out of her house, and asked me to follow them to their car. Like an idiot I gave the police officer the bunch of flowers then walked behind him. The wall was so high and menacing, no one in their right mind would dream of entering my territory. My garden was larger, safer and well sealed. I suddenly felt invisible.

I went in, drew all the curtains, ran upstairs, opened my suitcase and got the wooden box out.

Kalkelie, 2004

I would sit for hours next to my mother's grave under the fig tree. 'At least you are here, mother, in my own farm, rather than up there in Tira on your own. You keep me company here. Honouring you means burying you quickly, doesn't it? So rest in peace, mother, rest in peace.' My neighbour would come and say, 'You are not talking to your dead mother again. You did everything you could to bury her over there... come, come have some tea with us.'

When she died I washed her, wrapped her in white sash, put her in a coffin and asked everyone to help me take her back to her house in Tira. We hired a donkey cart, put the coffin in it, and walked in a procession to the gates. When we arrived there, we explained to them that it was a funeral and that the person who died owned a house in Tira and wanted to be buried there. They said we could not go out because the curfew was about to begin and that we needed two types of permissions to get through the gates and checkpoints. I pleaded with them to let me, my mother's body and the donkey through and send away the friends and relatives. I said I would carry her on my shoulders. How about if they buried her for me in the courtyard of our house? The soldiers smiled and shut the gate.

I washed my hands up to my elbows three times, gargled with water, blew my nose then washed my face. I was clean, pure and ready. I put on my white pilgrimage clothes, which I bought five years ago, and never wore. It was too expensive to travel all the way to Mecca to visit the prophet's grave, peace be upon him. I put on my white veil, making sure that every hair was well covered then I walked out of the cold storage room ready to be reunited with them.

Magna, AD 197-217

'Every night I ask the Mother of the gods, Ceres, dea Syria, who weighs life and laws in her balance, to protect you. I hope that you are well. I am unwell, coughing green mucus and blood all the hours of the day. Mea culpa. The dark rocks of Magna and the cold are as sharp as knives held close against your neck. I sit here defeated by two ferocious enemies, the weather and old age. I also cannot get a wink of sleep at night so I spend the time looking at the green glass of the small window, dreaming of a grand return to Antioch. When I walk through the door, you would be eating your breakfast by the fire. The minute you set your eyes on me you would recognise your father, your king, and the bowl drops out of your hand. I would run towards you, my son, my young master, hug you and kiss your forehead, your eyes, your hands, even your lovely feet. You would kiss the back of my hand. Your mother would hear us crying and would come out to greet her husband and lord. She would kiss my hands and head then put her arms around me, never to let me go again. We would walk in the warmth of the sun by the Orontes River, united, together, a family at last.

I left in pursuit of Roman citizenship so you can become a citizen too, proud, focused and educated. It was my call. If only I could last until I am granted full citizenship, but with the cold chills and the cough I am not so sure any more.

Sometimes I hear the cries of your dead baby sister. We placed her in a pot and buried her under the floor tiles of our house so her soul would not feel lonely.

This might be my last letter to you so goodbye, my young master. Kiss your mother's hands for me. Salutations to my brother and his children and all your loved ones!

Is it true that you have become a father?

Durham, 2004

The sun was about to rise and the lawn was covered with dew. With a pair of pliers I pulled the screws out, opened the wooden box, and unrolled the praying mat, looking for the soft tissue paper. Sometimes I heard it ticking. It fell out on the mat. It was about six centimetres long. Just before we buried him, I kept an eye on his body while my mother and grandmother were digging the grave. When I held his hand, which was covered with dry blood and dirt, I realised it had no nails, and that his little finger was dangling in the air so I pushed it back into place, but it came off in my hand. If my mum saw me she would have killed me. I wanted to throw it away, but instead I put it quickly in my pocket. Keeping his finger hidden turned out to be a life-long preoccupation and I had to work and travel under the shadow of my dead father's finger.

Now it was just three delicate slim bones. I placed the mat in the middle of the lawn, sat down and began digging a small hole. The birds began cooing their greeting to the morning. I placed the bones carefully in the hole, put the soil back and pressed it gently into place as if planting a delicate flower. I finally buried my father.

Dawn was about to break, so I stood up, pointed the compass glued to the mat towards Mecca, and placed my hands on top of each other on my tummy ready for the Morning Prayer. I heard the muezzin's call, so I knelt down to pray.

While reading a verse from the Qur'an I heard a strange sound. A dark hand carrying a gun appeared from behind the shed. Special Branch officers must have broken in. I rolled up the mat and said,

'I was not praying, honest.' Then I heard the click of the safety catch so I threw myself on the ground.

I lay there waiting for the trigger to be pulled, for the bullet to split my head open, but nothing happened. When I finally looked up there were no Special Branch agents, no guns, and no dark shadows in my garden. I, Khalid, was the only agent inside those walls.

Kalkelie, 2004

I said goodbye to my dead mother then went to bed, ready to leave. Pure, humble, perfumed and dressed in white linen, I lay in bed, waiting for the end. By now I had gotten used to the visits of old father suffocation. It was as if heavy slabs were placed right on top of your chest. 'I beg you, Allah, forgive my sins, don't leave me on this earth, take my soul tonight, unite me with them!' All I wanted, all I wished for, was to die in my sleep. I closed my eyes, hoping not to open them ever again.

When I heard the cock crowing, my heart broke.

I am indebted to Manal Mitri of Index on Censorship, and Marwan Omar for providing me with valuable documents on the Wall in Palestine.

Glass

By Wendy Robertson

Bettina sat very still. Something was moving above her, on the roof. Then she heard another, more muffled, persistent sound. She closed her eyes and behind her lids saw a soft, padded body that rolled from the apex of the roof then stopped, lodged against one of the big vicarage chimneys.

Her hand went towards the telephone then pulled away. Thomas would not exactly say she was an over-imaginative fool, but his voice would be drenched in its usual purring kindness, its characteristic moderation. These days, telephoning Thomas was a velvet-lined dead end. He lived in fear of her dark feelings and would rather drown in his good works than come home and find himself threshing about in her despair.

Phoning her doctor would be another dead end. *He* would come all right! He'd fill her full of chemicals, make her sleep for two days and forget everything. Including her name. And Orlando's name. And the name of the Chancellor of the Exchequer. They'd get out their clip-boards then, all right. Didn't that happen the other time?

Bettina made her way downstairs, through the charity sacks in the hall to the kitchen, where she cleared a small space in the clutter on the table so she could settle down there with her cup of tea. Now she could really hear the man overhead. A shadow loomed across the skylight. Shoes scraped and crunched on the flat roof.

She took a deep breath, reached up to the top shelf of the dresser and took down her glass egg. She rolled it between her hands to warm it, then held it up to catch the light from the skylight. The white spiral embedded within it started to shimmer; she could feel it pulsing against her palm.

The egg was a present from Orlando's godmother, who always bought gifts made in Sunderland. Local support was her watchword. Thomas had always been full of praise for her. Despite this, the egg was Bettina's favourite thing. It had certainly helped her to survive. Now, warmed by her hand, it started to buzz and hum. Then her body began to vibrate in tune with the egg and a bubble of light started in her solar plexus and slowly began to radiate upwards, outwards. Floating.

The floating feeling gave her the courage to look upwards and through the skylight she saw the shadowy outline of a body. She held the egg up towards the shadow: a temple offering. At that point the air was torn up by a great cracking sound. A body, bundled in a hooded parka, hurtled past her in an eruption of glass, wood and dust and dropped fair and square on the kitchen table. The boy lay very still, measuring his length on the six-foot table. Shards of glittering glass sat in the folds of his thick parka and a gash on his cheek was dripping blood. He was young – fifteen perhaps – and his sandy hair tumbled about his shoulders like the rays of the sun. His eyes were closed and he was out to the world.

Bettina reached out and eased his fingers away from the heavy screwdriver that he still clasped in his hand. Then, putting the egg in her mouth for safety, she rooted in a cupboard for some bits of old clothes line to tie his hands and his feet to the table legs.

Just as she – an ex-Guide who had always Been Prepared – finished tying her very effective reef knots, the boy's eyes fluttered open. He came to and started struggling against the ropes. His eyes widened with fear as he saw her looming above him, egg in mouth. 'Jesus!' he said.

'Jesus?' She removed the egg from her mouth. 'This is just the house to be saying that,' she said. The egg was warm and wet now. It had stopped vibrating.

'How's that?' he said, relieved that her face, without the bulging egg, looked relatively normal.

'Didn't you see the sign at the front gate? This is a vicarage?'

He whistled. 'Front gate? Never went down the front. I hitched down here from Gateshead, hopped across the dual carriageway and came across the gardens and in the back. This is the biggest house in this row. Good pickins in big houses. Me, I like Sunderland. Big houses, middle-sized houses, small streets and the sea, always the sea. It's got a canny buzz about it, Sunderland. But a vicarage? Looks like I'm wasting me time.' He pulled hard against his bonds. 'No need for these, missis. Never hurt a soul in my life. I'm tellen yer.' He opened his sapphire blue eyes really wide.

'How would I know that?'

'Teck my word for it.'

She laughed then. The laugh radiated round her head and suffused her body, making her feel lighter again, like the vibration of her egg. She looked down at it, rolling it from one hand to the other.

'What's that then, missis? That thing in yehr hand?'

'An egg, idiot! Don't you know an egg when you see one?'

'I thought yeh wor incubating it when I saw yeh with it in yehr mouth. Don't some animals do that with their young?' His face imploded in a combined nod-and-wink and lost its built-in beauty. 'Yeh dinnet seem like any vicar's wife to me, missis.'

She laughed again and pushed back her thick unkempt hair. Perhaps she should untie the boy. He hardly seemed dangerous.

'Let's loose, missis,' he said softly.

She nearly did as he said, but instead, she drew a chair up close to the table. 'Perhaps I should tend to that cut first,' she said placidly. 'Don't want you to bleed to death do we?'

'That'd be a start. Yeh got a plaster or something?'

She looked vaguely round the kitchen. 'I'm not sure.'

He lifted up his head and looked round with some difficulty. 'This place is a fucken mess, missis,' he said, glaring at her. She noticed again the blueness of those eyes, the thick fair lashes fanning upwards. 'Doesn't it bother yeh?'

She shrugged. 'There seems so little time. Little time to do things.' She yawned very widely.

'Yeh're on sommat', missis, en't yeh?' His voice was sharp.

'On something?'

'Pills, substances. That kind of thing.'

She shrugged. 'They push them on me.'

'Don't you take them, that's my advice. Never touch'm meself. Places where I've been there's loads of people pushing stuff on yeh, legal and illegal. They wanter dumb yeh down, friends and foes alike.'

She stared at him. 'And what are these places where've you been?'

'Homes, then schools with bars and fat lads with janglin' key...' He lifted his head again so he could look her in the eye. 'Come on, missis. Undo me hands at least. It's fucken murder tied up like this. Me leg's in cramp. Look at it! It's shivering of its own accord?'

'Did you really never take any of that stuff?' Bettina did occasionally read a paragraph in Thomas's *Guardian*. Drugs were rife in those places. 'The stuff they pushed on you?'

A shake of the head. 'Nah. Never. Hard going not to, but.'

She leaned across and undid the offending foot and rubbed his leg absently. 'So how did you end up in those places? And why did you rain in on me like manna from heaven?'

'Misspent youth, missis. Bunked off school early days. Mam and Dad had other things on their minds. Dad always on the pop. Then Mam went off her lid and they took her away. Me, I did a bit of grafting. Why, man, the fucken things were laid there for yeh, asking to be taken. But then the mate I was grafting with grasses on us to save his neck, doesn't he? So I end up in Castington with the bad lads.'

'And now you end up here,' she said, primmer than she felt. 'Plunging in on me like manna from heaven. Why the roof? Why not a door or window?'

'They don't spot it, missis, if you get in on the roof. Not for days.'

'Well, I spotted it, didn't I?'

He groaned. 'Don't do it missis! Don't tell on us. Me sister-in-law's thrown us out and me brother's putty in her painted hands. And with no address I get no fucken dole, see?' He flexed his free knee up to his chest. 'And if yeh lay us in now, missis, they'll have us away for a long time. I'm supposed to be good, or else! I just thought a little light grafting'd get us the money for the fare to Edinburgh. I've a mate there who's promised us a job. He sells kites on the Royal Mile and needs another pair of hands.'

'Kites?'

'So, what's yehr name?' he interrupted.

She was surprised into an answer. 'Bettina,' she said.

'Bettina? Funny old name, that.'

'After a fashion model.'

'Like that Naomi, yeh mean?'

'Well, more old style, really. High heels and New Look.'

'I know that. Retro. The painted sister-in-law has magazines. Retro's right back in now.' He grinned up at her appealingly. 'Now, Bettina. What about the other foot?'

She shook her head. 'I might be retro, dear, but I'm not out of the ark.'

He lay back. The blood on his cheek was congealing. He changed tack. 'If you untie me I'll clear all this mess up for yeh. It's like a fucken packin' can in here.'

She threw the egg from hand to hand. 'It's all too hard. I can't even start.'

He nodded, straining his head up from the table to catch her eye properly. 'My mam was just like that before they carted her away. And so was I when I was thirteen. I bunked off school and lay around the house all day. Couldn't stop yawning. Then, when I started a bit of graftin', I was all right again. Didn't feel so bad at all. Not so tired, like.'

'Are you suggesting I try a bit of gentle grafting?'

He raised his head again and laughed at this, his golden hair lifting and settling in the light from the broken window. 'Nah. It worked for me, like. One time I had this counsellor called Gretchen. Posh lass. She said my trouble was adrenaline. Too intelligent. Not enough to do. The adrenaline kind of goes bad. At least I think that's what she said. She had great legs, that one. Right up to her armpits.'

Bettina put the egg back in her mouth and started to root in a drawer.

His eyes followed her. 'Yeh look fucken weird with that in your mouth, Bettina. If yeh dinnet mind us saying so.'

She took it out of her mouth and placed it carefully in a pink egg cup on the second shelf of the kitchen unit. 'It's kind of comforting,' she said. She pulled out a drawer, tipped the contents onto the floor and fished a tin of plasters out of the mess. Then she took a baking bowl and filled it with warm water, found an only slightly-soiled towel and set about cleaning the cut on the boy's face.

He lay back on the table and relaxed as she dabbed his cheek. 'So, what family d'you have, Bettina?'

'Well, I don't know what counts. I did have a son, Orlando. He's fifteen. But he's not here now.'

'Orlando? I thought that was a cat.' He whistled. 'But your Orlando, he's not here now?'

She shook her head. 'No.'

'Did he, is he... er... ? He isn't dead is he?' The boy was staring at her, unblinking.

She shook her head. 'He's at school in Durham. He lives there. Then for holidays he goes to his aunt, my husband's sister in Barnard Castle.'

'Special Needs? A lad in my class had Special Needs. Couldn't read a letter, couldn't hold a pencil. Had to go off to a living-in school too.'

'No. No. Orlando's very clever. He doesn't have Special Needs.'
She peeled the backing off the plaster and covered the cleaned
wound. 'Unless his Special Need is to be away from me.'

'Why's that? Why'd he need to be away from you?'

She was silent for a moment. Her glance strayed to the egg but she
resisted the impulse to pick it up. 'They said I tried to smother him
when he was little. He was nearly dead when they found him. I didn't
do it, but there was no telling them. They were very kind, of course.
Thomas – my husband – says I was lucky. That anyone else would
have ended up behind bars. Even so I was angry with them all
because they were wrong to take him away. I tried to tell them, him,
the doctors and the police. They didn't like me protesting. *Hysteria*.
It's in my notes.'

'That's why they push all the junk into you? To stop you squarking?'

She tore her glance from the egg and turned quickly to stare at
him. 'Yes, I suppose they do.'

'Tell them no. Keep telling them. Dinnet take it.'

'Trying to say no to Thomas is like saying no to a billow of
blancmange.'

He laughed at this. 'Yeh're fucken sound, Bettina. I tell yeh that.'
He peered up at her. 'Go on, Bettina. Let us loose and I'll help yeh
clear all this up. Promise.' He smiled. The light streaming through the
shattered skylight glinted again on the fine bloom of hair on his cheek.

He was irresistible. She took a deep breath and started to untie
him. In minutes he was sitting up on the table rubbing his wrists.
Then he jumped down and loomed up before her. For the first time
she realised just how tall he was. They stared at each other for a long
time. Then he clapped his hands together hard and she jumped. 'Just
to get the blood runnin', like,' he grinned. He looked round,
shrugged himself out of his parka and draped it over the back of a
chair. 'Now then, where's yehr bin, Bettina? You got plastic bags?
Dustpan and brush?'

So together they swept and brushed, bagged and heaved the
detritus into the back yard. Then, at the boy's insistence, they tackled
the kitchen surfaces and the mountains of dirty dishes and pans. In
three hours, order reigned in the sprawling vicarage kitchen.

'Now then,' the boy fished in his pocket and pulled out a battered
notebook and scribbled in it with a stubby pencil. He tore off the

page and gave it to Bettina. 'Me Uncle Ted. Lives down Hendon. Them low houses. You ring him, Bettina. He'll board up the skylight for now and then rebuild it for yeh later. Yeh'll have to pay, like. But he's cheap. Cash only, like.'

Bettina hesitated. She had not telephoned anyone except Thomas and her doctor for many years.

He stared at her, nodded, and picked up the phone. 'Here, I'll do it for yeh.'

She clicked on the kettle and went out to the hall to rummage in an old handbag under the stairs and came back with a leather wallet in her hand. She counted out four twenty-pound notes onto the table. 'For services rendered. Should get you to Edinburgh so you can sell those kites,' she said, smoothing them out in a row. 'I only hope they're still legal tender.'

He was pouring boiling water over bags into a tall beaker. 'Why's that?' he said.

'They're old. I was going out to buy myself a new spring coat when that business happened, when it all blew up. When they took Orlando. I've never been out of the house since.'

He handed her the beaker of tea. 'Time yeh got yourself out a bit, Bettina. Remember the adrenaline! Goes fucken bad if you lie around too much. Don't I know it?' He gulped his tea. 'Yeh should teck it steady but mebbe you should go and see him. That Orlando.'

'They won't let me. He...'

'He'll be dying to see yeh. I know it.'

'You can't say that.'

He scowled at her. 'I can. Me, I'm dying to see me own mother at this very minute. But I have to go through all those locked doors at Cherry Knowle to do that.'

She knew the hospital. She had been there briefly. Thomas made pastoral visits there. 'Well, I...' Her glance wandered away from him and alighted again on the egg in the pink egg cup.

The boy took her face in his large hands and turned it towards him, away from the egg. 'Yeh should take your time, like I said, Bettina. Give yourself time but just say yeh're gunna see him. For definite.'

When he moved his hands away, her cheeks felt very cold. It was years since Thomas had even tolerated her touch, flesh on flesh.

The boy picked up the money and tucked it into the pocket of his parka. 'Ta for this,' he said. He looked round. 'Now then, what about dinner?'

'I don't usually...'

'You sit there, drink your tea and I'll rustle something up.'

For the next twenty minutes he rustled round the kitchen like a whirlwind. He found two dusty tins of corned beef, one of carrots, and two squashed Oxo cubes. He poured boiling water on the Oxo cubes, peeled some old potatoes then arranged everything with some care in a Pyrex casserole dish which he put in the top oven of the Aga. 'Fifty minutes,' he said. 'I've set yehr timer.' He stood grinning down at her.

At last she started to feel uneasy. She tucked the stray hair back again under its clip. 'Thomas will be back by then,' she lied. 'Perhaps you'd join us?'

'That's nice but no thanks, Bettina.' He stood up. 'I'd better be off. I got a train to catch. Fucken kites to fly.' He put on his parka and zipped it up. 'I'll call on me uncle down Hendon and tell him about this, then hitch a lift back to Gateshead.'

She stood, reached across and took the egg from its pink cup. She thrust it into his hand, curling his fingers over it with her palm. 'You take this. Treasure it,' she said. 'P'raps you could give it to your mother.'

He looked at the egg, nodded and thrust it into his pocket beside the money. Then she saw him off, waving at him from the door as though he were any routine caller at the vicarage.

It was only as she turned round that she realised the boy had not volunteered his name. Still, she wondered about him, who he really was; whether he was really going to Edinburgh.

'Oh, Bettina!' When Thomas answered the phone his voice was threaded with its usual pleading, gentle panic.

'Thomas?' she said, pleased at her own brisk tone. 'I'm afraid the kitchen ceiling's collapsed... No, no. That won't be necessary. I have arranged for someone to come and make a temporary mend. No... he's coming round as I speak. He'll mend it properly as soon as possible... No, no, I'm quite all right. Quite... Thomas? Thomas?'

My Auntie Milly's house never changes. Like a doll's house in a row of dolls' houses. Just one storey high; a door, two windows and a steep roof. Some of the houses in the row have windows cut into the roofs these days, but they look like scars to me. My auntie's house has a flat skylight. My uncle keeps his fish tanks up there.

'Your Uncle Ted's gone off to do that job you rang about...' Auntie Milly makes an arc in the air with her cigarette as she lets me in. 'Who is this woman?'

'Bettina,' I say. It's a nice name, canny. 'Cash job...'

'Bettina? Funny name that.' She leads me into her small downstairs room and parks herself in the chair that still has the imprint of her bottom on the frayed cushion. She holds out a battered packet of Superkings and frowns when I turn her offer down. Like I told Bettina, I don't take no substances. Then she lights a new one herself from the stub of the old one. She takes a deep drag and speaks through the streaming smoke. 'You know this woman?'

'You could say that. I do now, anyway.'

'You're a funny'n, you. I always said that. I told your mam. You've bred a funny'n there, Anne Marie. Always cleaning.'

I look round. Aunt Milly's room is neat enough. It smells like our own first house: *pot-pourri*, old fat, burnt gas, dead fires and cigarette smoke. When I was little I loved to come home to that smell and watch my mother put her cigarette to smoulder in a saucer while she made me my tea. She used to talk to me a lot in those days and could really make me laugh.

Then there was the meltdown and Mam took to her couch. She began to see things that weren't there and the room became a war zone around her. Everything dissolved into something different, like when you hit the wrong knob on the telly and it changes from colour to black and white. My brother and me tried to clean up around her and make her cups of tea to keep her calm. My dad finally lit off and only came back when she was sectioned and the police tracked him down. That was it for us. The end of the beginning.

Auntie Milly's my mother's younger sister, though you'd think she was older. The last time I saw my mother she was full-faced, smooth-skinned and young-looking, even though her glance was vacant and her shuffling way of walking made her seem older. That was down to the substances, like, if you ask me.

Milly's sharp eyes rake over me. 'What brings you down Sunderland? In bother are yeh, son?'

'No such thing, Auntie. Just down here for a visit.'

'Workin' are yeh?'

'Yer jokin'!'

She arcs her cigarette again, leaving a trail of smoke. 'You should stay on down here. We'd find you a space. Teddy'd find you some work.'

I'm already shaking my head. 'Wouldn't suit, Auntie. You an me both know Ted can't stand the sight of me.' There have been various incidents down the years, mostly when he has bad-mouthed my mam or my dad. My Uncle Ted's your upright, hard-working kind of feller. The man collects fish. Need I say more?

'So, you're down to see our Anne Marie?' Milly peers up at me through the smoke that is sitting in the air. 'Gunna visit That Place?'

I stare at her, wanting to deny it. Out of the blue, I'm back in our old house, on the night it all really started. I've got the kettle on ready to make my mam a cup of tea when she gets in from the bingo. We've had two days of snow and the night's dark and freezing, But it's all right. The gas fire's on, my dad's safely out at the pub and my brother's at scouts. I hear the click of the gate as Mam comes in the back yard, then there is this awful racket. Nine cats leap out at her, meowing and howling to get past her through the gate. They've been sheltering in the igloo I've just built between the wash house and the wheelie bin. I've been playing out there all day, building the igloo and making a dry seat from two piles of bricks and a cut-down wooden pallet.

Mam's screams pull me outside pronto into the narrow yard. She's lying there in the snow beside my igloo, shuddering and retching. I touch her shoulder but she's already gone, leapt through the night skies onto another planet where I can't reach her.

When I think about it, that was probably the beginning of the end of the beginning. It was after that night that she took to her couch.

'Will you go and see her?' Milly persists.

My hand, thrust hard in the pocket of my parka, encounters the egg. 'Aye. I think so.' I turn to go.

'Mebbe you'd like a cup of tea?' Milly ventures.

'Nah. I'll get off,' I say.

The day room smells of piss, Shake n' Vac and cheap shampoo. It reminds me of the reception area at Newcastle Airport, where I went once to meet my dad off the Aberdeen flight when he was on the rigs. Artificial flowers, too many seats and not much else.

The men and women wandering through here are a bit like travellers. They have no luggage but are clearly in transit. A girl in a green overall, who looks like someone from 5C, takes me across to my mother, who is sitting with her back to the room, looking out of the window. 'Look, Anne Marie. You've got a visitor, pet.'

The girl looks at me, her eyebrows raised.

'She's my mother,' I say helpfully.

'Here's your son come to see you, Anne Marie.'

Mam's head turns and she looks at me, smiling slightly. Someone's done her hair up in thick black coils. Her clothes are immaculate. She is wearing powder and pink lipstick. This is a relief. The last time I came she was walking around with her dress tucked in her knickers, all very innocent.

The girl in the green overall is still standing there looking down at her. 'We're all in our best today, aren't we, Anne Marie? The Minister came this afternoon. From the Government.' She turns to me. 'Sommat about funding.'

Mam looks up at her. 'Get away, will you, lass? This is me own son. Isn't that what you said? Leave us alone.'

The girl stalks away and I sit down on a hard chair by the window. 'Hello, Mam,' I say.

She frowns at me. 'Who d'she say you were?'

I look into her dark eyes, my flesh all goosepimples. Here we go. She frightens me. Every time I see her I feel this fear that makes my hair stand on end.

She's not happy with my silence. 'Why d'you come?' she says sharply. 'Son?'

I dip in my pocket and hold out the egg. 'I brought you this egg. It's made of glass.'

She holds it up into a beam of sunlight and the spiral shimmers. 'I sold these, son, years ago when I worked in Binns. Very popular, they were. They flew off the shelves.' She turns it upside down, staring at it with her head on one side. 'What a lovely thing it is.'

I think of Bettina with the egg in her mouth.

'Thank you, son.' Mam looks me straight in the eye. 'What's that plaster? Have you hurt yourself? Shouldn't you be at school?

I have two sons, you know. Two sons of my own. They go to school.'

I stand up quickly and the chair tips up behind me. 'I have to go.'

'You're going. Why are you going?' Her voice is young, high-toned like a bird.

'I have to go and fly some kites.' I start to walk quickly down the long room.

Her voice travels after me. 'Kites? Kites? Lovely, that. Kites!'

At the door I turn round again but she is concentrating on the egg, turning it this way and that in the light from the window.

I am nearly at the gates when the girl in the green overall catches up with me. She thrusts the egg into my hand. 'She can't have this,' she says.

'Why not?' I say. 'It's a gift.'

'It's glass,' she says. 'Glass is not allowed. You won't believe what they get up to, with glass. It's very dangerous. You should think on.' She pauses. 'We had to wrestle it off her you know. That glass thing got her quite excited. They had to sedate her.'

'Right,' I say, pushing it deep into the pocket of my parka. 'I suppose you're right.'

Then, her still standing there, I turn and set off to run, making for the dual carriageway, thumb at the ready.

After Life

By Sara Maitland

Cuthbert of Lindisfarne, bishop-monk, hermit, friend, missionary, thaumaturge, great saint of the North, was born in 634 and trained as a monk at Melrose. After the Synod of Whitby in 663-64, he spent much of his energy restabilising the church that had been seriously disrupted by the success of the universalist party led by Wilfred. Colman, Abbot of Lindisfarne, and many of the monks from this centre of northern Christianity felt unable to accept the changes and departed to Ireland. Cuthbert, who was at Whitby, accepted the king's decisions and worked to restore and expand harmony in the North East. From 676 he was a hermit in the Farne Islands for nine years, then a bishop for two, and finally returned to his island hermitage to die in 687.

This is the beginning of the story. After that... after that there is no story. The silence of eternity has no narrative. The wind blows and the tides wax and wane under the moon. The interfolded, entwining, intricate lines maze round and over and under and through. They do not end, they come back to the beginning and the end is the beginning is the end.

His posthumous fame grew. Eleven years after he died, the Lindisfarne community decided, as was normal practice, to elevate his bones to a more public shrine. But on opening the coffin his body was found to be incorrupt: rust and moth had not consumed nor time like a thief broken in and stolen. His body was not decomposed, rotted, putrescent, desiccated nor in anyway decayed.

This miracle inspired a profound devotion to the saint. For nearly 200 years he was enshrined at Lindisfarne in great honour. In 875 however, Lindisfarne was threatened by a Viking attack. Not for the first time – ten years earlier, Lindisfarne had been devastated by the Norsemen, many of its treasures stolen, and many members of the community killed. They could not face it again and decided to escape, taking Cuthbert with them. They opened the coffin and placed other important relics in it with Cuthbert's body, and took to the hills. For seven years the coffin and its bearers roamed northern England and south west Scotland, seeking a safe asylum. Eventually they settled in Chester-le-Street for nearly a century, before further Viking raids sent them on their travels again.

In 995 they finally reached Durham. After the conquest a new Norman cathedral was built for Durham and in 1104 Cuthbert's remains were translated into it. Once again his coffin was opened and his body examined and found to be unaffected by four hundred years and much journeying. At the Reformation the shrine was dismantled, with a view to burning the saint's bones, according to Reformation practice. However, the commissioners were so shaken by discovering that the body was still unaffected that, after writing to London for special instructions, they reburied the bones under the now dismantled shrine.

In 1828 the grave was reopened. The bones were found bare and dry as might have been expected, the treasures removed to a museum and the saint buried again and, so far or finally, left in peace.

In heaven he rejoices to be with the hermits. They sit back to back, leaning against and so supporting each other. They shift slightly so that the knobbly protuberances of their spiritual spines fit into each other like the pieces of a jigsaw puzzle, their thin hard souls in perfect, silent companionship. He never has to be with priests, monks, abbots or bishops, because in heaven, thank heaven, those things neither matter nor count. But sometimes, except that here there is no time, he finds himself with the other members of the Sea Green Society and despite the name, which ought to please him, he grows as near to irritability and dislike as is possible for a blessed saint. The other members are, to his harsh and disciplined heart, too often neurasthenic Italian girls with a tendency to giggle. He feels slightly embarrassed, and then ashamed of himself. To be truthful, he finds incorruptibility vulgar – it offends his fierce purity.

He died quietly in the arms of his friend Herefrith. Outside, his monks were keeping vigil for him, singing the fifty-ninth psalm. As was proper. Then the trouble started and it was his own fault. Never give in to the demands of love. He should have known better but he had been weary, in pain, alone for too long, wrestling with the enemy, pleading with his God. His resistance worn down, he rescinded his demand to be buried here in his own place, on the island at the edge of the void.

His soul went home. In the dark morning hours, on the turning of the tide.

But they take his body back to Lindisfarne, to the Holy Island. They bury it with honour. Treasure it. Beg for miracles. And God of course hears their need and does not consult his. Incorruptibility is a faith-enhancing, joy-giving powerful miracle. God *would*.

The sublimity of the saint's earthly life was well attested by his numerous miracles. Almighty God in his providence now chose to give further proof of Cuthbert's glory in heaven by putting into the mind of the brothers to dig up his bones. They expected to find the bones quite bare (as is usual with the dead), the rest of the body having dwindled to dust... On opening the coffin they found the body completely intact, looking as though still alive, and the joints of the limbs still flexible. It seemed not dead but sleeping.

Still the wind comes in, harsh, unrelenting, from the east across the huge grey sea. It carries flotsam from Nordic wrecks; great flights of geese from the ice circle; and the sharp acrid stench of blood and grease that comes on the tide, swelling under the bows of the square-sailed Viking ships.

He is caught, like a fly in web, a web of love and need and tenderness.

At least the love which bound him to them is useful to them. The community grows rich in his prestige. But in the end his love is not enough, not enough to cast out their fear, to set them free or to make them indifferent to material possessions – the funny mossy-soft thing that is his useless but incorrupt body. When they hear the Viking ships are in the Tyne estuary again, terror strikes deep and sharp. Foolish panic, rat-like scuffling in the church, sharper breaths, hoarse cries and tears.

He does not want to go. On the storm wind, in the strong tide pushing the longships up onto the mud flats, in the screams and smoke of their approaching rampage, he hears the song of the storm woman coming in to set him free.

They are concerned that the Norsemen will burn and destroy his shrine, his body, their treasure. It doesn't matter. 'It doesn't matter,' he wants to shout out, but cannot. They love him too much and not enough. He cannot leave them. His spirit grunted, cross and weary.

In their panic they open his coffin, shove in their other great treasures. They have to tip him over onto his side so he can no longer even look up at the huge blue sky and the wild clouds. He is wedged in by King Oswald's skull. This makes him smile.

Through the night, carrying him far too carefully, they flee into the hills. From there they can look down and see the orange shadow of the flames, which smudge the darkness; smell the sharp tang, which is smoke and flesh together; congratulate themselves on their wisdom and promptness. All night there is fierce burning, stripping away riches, beauty, serenity, rootedness. Above them the moon still shines, ducking in and out of silver clouds and high, cold, unmoved, the stars sing their ancient silent song. The wind runs over the grasses of the hills, the heather stirs and the many waters slip over the edge, heading with rattling determination towards the sea and their own dissolution. None of them notice those things, none of them look up or around. They look down in terror at the looting; and at his coffin with a desperate self-seeking love. He cannot leave them.

It is better on the long journey. Under his shoulder is the hard round skull of the noble Oswald, Aidan's friend. Stripped bare and bold. It forces him to lie on his side as he would never have let his novices lie. The monks, his children, carry him on their shoulders as they climb high into the hills, with the long views of nothing, the cold wind, and the slow drift of gulls. They settle nowhere. They grow lean and hard and hardy. Sowing but not gathering and free as the foxes which sniff around at night.

They think they will follow Colman home to Ireland and so they trek their slow way across the rough mountains, and down to the western coast. Ireland is so full of God's servants and relics and miracles, that he thinks they will not need him there and he might be set free. They take ship, secretly, on those brackish seas, but - as the land vanished into the grey rain - he hears the cry of his people, a great wailing of childish need and despair. The people he was called to love. And he hears the dark voice of the storm woman far to the east, riding the longer swell of her fiercer sea. So they have to go back. A storm drives them back.

Still the rivers come down, tumultuous, laughing, from the high moors to the west. They curl, curve, carve across the low lands. They hurl themselves against all the long waves. Fresh and salt mixing; pushing against each other. Only Farne is free of it all. Free of direction, thrust, purpose. Free of cities, ambitions, power, time, greed and longing. The tide rises and falls. The wind comes and goes. The long swells give storm or silence in a rhythm that rocks his prayers and sets him free.

He should have stayed. He should not have given in. He should have insisted, been buried there, stayed a few seasons and been washed away. They were always the great betrayals - the betrayals in love and tenderness. With a kiss.

Sometimes he wishes he had committed some nice juicy sin. A real sin of the flesh, a stinking sin of corruption. The trouble was that women have never really much interested him, at least not in that way. He hears those sins, sees how they shake his brothers. He listens attentively but without understanding. He can only feel a wide compassion and tolerance, which is never the response they want.

There are only two women in his life.

Hild, old enough to be his mother, who shares with him a sort of distance, a detached hilarity through the long synod meetings at Whitby. He holds by instinct, by training and by love to Columba's rule, Columba's Easter, Aidan's gentle holiness. But... once he looks away from Colman's grief; avoids looking at Wilfred's determination. Instead, suddenly, he catches Hild's glance, her deep smile. Games, foolish games. Hild who teaches him there, without words, in a silent smile, that although it is all genuinely, terribly important, it really does not matter very much. She gives him freedom; and one long evening the two of them listen to Caedmon singing the huge ancient stories of the faith in his own, their own, language, a gift to the poor, regardless of the date of Easter or the shape of the tonsure. He smiles whenever he thinks of Hild.

And there is the storm woman.

There are other sins of course, juicier than seeking a little comfort in the arms of another against the cold nights of the soul. There is love of wealth; blasphemy; discourtesy to the poor – or indeed to Kings, to one's own brothers, to any created thing. There is violence, arrogance of office and of mind; self-serving anger; withholding consolation; impenitence; apostasy. There is always pride. And the mysterious sin against the Holy Spirit, which can never be forgiven, whatever it may be. It is not that he has not sinned, but he has failed to sin with enough energy or commitment. Cursed are the pure in heart, they are doomed to incorruptibility. He cannot abandon the people, and the harsh habits of love.

He has never seen the storm woman, but she comes. She comes straight as the wind from the cold lands of dawn, and she rides the long grey swell in from the long grey sea. She is without pity, ruthless. She is not bound by love and compassion, she is free. Her fierce freedom strikes a chord in him, low and unsettling. She stands before the mast and the wind blows her hair towards him, plaited, interwoven as the pages of his lovely book, but alive and wild. She treads on the lion and the dragon; the young lion and dragon she tramples under her feet. She is clothed not with the sun but with the storm, and the sword and the wild.

The longship surfs in fast on a white roll of spume and spray, swoops into the bay and they drop the square sail. She does not waver. She spreads her arms out in greeting. She is black and blood red and she brings the brands for the burning – for the stripping down, the purging, the looting, the making of deserts. He sees her even in the dark. He sees her stretched out, the mast and boom behind her is her cross. She is a wild Christ to him, from a heroic people, crucified, harrowing hell, rejoicing on the far side of destruction. He wants her; he wants to go out to her across the breaking waves. To walk to her on the water and share her blood-stained laughter. He understands her dark joy. Here we have no abiding city, he thinks; here we have only wooden long ships with their dragon prows, storming heaven with a fierce blood lust.

To us otters he was otter.

He was otter in the economy of his movement. Humans fidget. But he was an otter.

Silent and still when he was not moving. Swift and sleek when he moved. He slid into the water like an otter, swam so quietly; stood all night while stars wheeled overhead, and the night waves lapped at his shoulders. He was otter: defenceless, innocent, playful. He laughed as an otter laughs, deep inside and silently. He was otter, weightless, graceful and free in the water and the cold did not reach into the depths of his belly. He stayed in the sea all night.

He was otter but he had no fur. When he came out the water we could see he was cold. We warmed him and he blessed us. Why be surprised? That is no miracle, not as otters think.

The heavy weight of Durham Cathedral pins him down.

He makes a terrible mistake. For over a hundred years they settle in Chester-le-Street and he tries to settle with them and enjoy prosperity, to offer his support to a new style bishop who lives like a king. But he hears the storm woman calling, and smells the Viking smell and they are on the road again. He wants to go back to Farne, to the wind and the sea. He wants his body to disintegrate gently the way other bodies do. Dust to dust, to dissolve into the water, his bones powdered into the fine sand. They travel northward again, and he hears a curlew in the mist, sees a river curl, curl around a standing rock. He thinks it is an island. He thinks he can be free there. The mist is dense; they are lost and longing for supper.

'Mmmmoooooo, ooooo,' calls the dun cow out of the mist. 'Moooo,' she lows, longing to let down, to have the warm milk pulled out of her gently and to feel the milkmaid's forehead pressed against her flank in the arm byre. He sees an island, hears a dun cow longing to go home. He yearns towards the standing rock with the water all around it. His soft flesh sinks towards his island – towards a silence that will let his flesh flow out of him like milk. He is cow. God is his milkmaid, pulling the soft flesh out of him. Soft, warm, milky as a child. He will travel no farther. Here is his resting place.

He is wrong. It is not an island. The tight loop of the river leaves a neck of land – like Lindisfarne, not Farne. The desire of his incorrupt body and the tenderness of his heart betray him again.

But they take him to Durham, which is not island but fortress. Its heavy weight, and the weight of people's love and need pin him down. The cathedral is heavy over him. He wants to be free of it, and charity demands that he is not. Actually he never liked Wilfred. Hild is right and the date of Easter does not matter, because Christ is risen, alleluia, and running wild and free in the dark night. Hild is right because someone was going to be hurt. Colman's hurt is sad but Wilfred's hurt would be dangerous. None of these things matter, but stone churches matter. They pin him down, Wilfred's stone churches.

Here we have no abiding city. The clear line of hill or horizon abides. It is constant and it holds the silence. The line that divides earth and sky, clear and clean, also unites them. And it abides. It emerges out of the dark in the first dawn light and is swallowed back into the dark at nightfall. Above the line, infinity; below the line mortality. But the line itself is both, and holds them both and the wind blows along hill or sea, fresh and free like the passage of the spirit. That is where he wants to be, dust to dust, blown along the edge of the wild. Not pinned here in a splendid tomb weighed down by a stone church.

They spend over one hundred years building a church grand enough for their idea of him.

The Abbot of Seez, unwrapping with the aid of the local brethren, the covering of the venerable head, raised it a little in both his hands

209

in the sight of everyone, and bending it about in different directions, found it adhering to the rest of the body, with all the neck joints perfect. Then, taking hold of an ear, he waggled it backwards and forwards with some degree of force. He found the whole body with its nerves and bones solid and covered with soft flesh. He also shook it and raised it so high that it almost appeared to sit in its quiet abode. Moreover he also took care to examine into the perfect state of its feet and legs. But there were some who now exclaimed that he had carried proof of the truth further than was required. So raising his voice he announced, 'Behold, brothers, this body lies here, lifeless indeed but as sound and entire as on that day on which the soul left it to wing its flight to heaven.'

No escape. He is lumbered with incorruptibility.

And then at last the blessed commissioners come. He loves their harsh commitment, their untiring zeal for their Lord. He loathes their theology of course, but Hild's deep smile had taught him that although theology was all genuinely, terribly important, it really did not matter very much. They are like the Norsemen, set upon freedom and ferocity. They have a savage contempt for his body that he shares with them. Carelessly they break his leg with a hammer. 'Chuck the bones down,' they shout.

Before the Crown took possession of the church and monastery of Durham, the royal commissioners had defaced the shrine of St Cuthbert. The commissioners were Dr Ley, Dr Henley and Mr Blythman. After the spoil of his ornaments and jewels, and finding the chest he lay in very strongly bound with iron, the goldsmith took a great fore-hammer and did break the said chest. When they opened the chest they found him lying whole, incorrupt, with his face bare and his beard as if it had been a fortnight's growth.

Then when the goldsmith saw that he had smashed one of his legs when he broke into the chest, he was very sorry for it and cried out, 'Alas I have broken one of his legs.'

Dr Henley called up to him and told him to throw down the bones. The goldsmith answered that he could not get them asunder for the sinews and skin held them. Dr Ley climbed up to see if this was true and then called back to Dr Henley that Cuthbert was lying whole.

Dr Henley would give this no credit and again called out, 'Chuck down the bones.'

Mr Ley replied, 'If you don't believe me, come up and see for yourself.'

Finally Dr Henley stepped up and handled the body and saw that he was whole and uncorrupt. So they ordered him to be carried to the vestry and kept securely there until they could find out what the king wanted done with him. When they heard from the king, the prior and monks buried him in the ground underneath where his shrine had been.

Dear Dr Henley, sweet, kind, merciful Dr Henley and all his ilk. No excessive respect, no childlike, clinging love that holds the flesh in bondage and will not let it go back to the source and be forgotten. Burn the bones, Dr Henley, as you burned Thomas' and Edmund's - ashes to ashes. Why him? The great saints, the true saints, were not held captive. Aidan's body was not incorrupt. The great apostle Peter's body was not incorrupt. Wilfred's - he hardly hesitates, he knows that Wilfred was a very great saint; that is quite different from liking him - Wilfred's body was not incorrupt. This is so unfair, Wilfred would have loved incorruptibility. Another excuse for another stonking great stone church. There had been a plan once to enshrine him with Wilfred at Ripon. Wilfred would not have liked that. Nor would he.

The commissioners have set him free. They shove his body back into an ordinary grave and dismantle the shrine and laugh. They do not need him. They do not love him. They do not want him. He laughs at their impertinent indifference. He can go now. Deep below his new grave he can hear the waters rushing, curling round the peninsular, washing away at hard rock and sanctuary and tomb.

Pulling, pulling him towards the sea. At last.

His body dissolves.

Dust to dust.

His body dissolves into the great nothing - of cloud formations, of curlews and terns, and of winds. The nothing pulls him in. The arms of the storm woman hold him. There is silence.

The line of the moor holds the silence.

There is no narrative in silence. The interfolded, entwining, intricate lines of life maze round and over and under and through. They do not end, they come back to the beginning and the end is the beginning is the end. The sea deep is the spume of the waves is the foam in the wind is the billow of the clouds is the rain on the spring crops is the stillness of the well is spilled on the ground is flowing back into the depths of the sea.

The words drop away

                         into the ocean

                                                          of

silence

The Great Big Book Exchange

By Paul Magrs

There was once a woman who loved to read.

There was once a woman whose daughter went and left home and died. Now the old woman had a house filled with paperback books, one cantankerous old man, and one orphaned grandson.

There was once a woman who lived in a small town at the top of a hill. There was a market place, two pubs, an Italian cafe... there were low, flat fields criss-crossed by railway tracks and country roads, a sandstone quarry, the old pit nearby... This was her landscape.

There was once a woman who had read so many paperbacks that she couldn't possibly remember all that she had read. So much of it leaked out of her head, under the gap at the bottom of her bedroom door, across the top landing, down the staircase...

There was once a woman who was a dinner lady in the school her grandson had to go to now. Where he didn't fit in, because he'd slipped back a whole generation into the past. His parents had been killed in a plane crash. A holiday in Florida they'd won on a quiz show. Everyone dreams of going to America. Tickets and new luggage and kisses at Teesside airport and they were never seen again. The tape of their quiz show triumph sat by the video recorder on the stone-effect fire place. No one had ever watched it.

There was a woman who loved to sit up all night reading. She would ward off the present she was in with reading.

There was a woman who didn't remember the names of people, the order that events came in, the twists of plots. She could never remember the outcomes of who was in love and who was dead and buried or married; or who was saved and who deserved or didn't deserve their comeuppance.

There was once a woman called Winnie who knew that, even if she forgot the adventures she'd been on, or the lives she'd lived, the paperbacks were still there to prove it. This woman was measuring her life's duration in inch-thick spines.

There was a woman who believed that books, old books, had a life of their own. She believed they were independent of their owners and they floated from home to home. They rested, like pigeons taking a

213

breather, in book shops and market stalls. She believed they sought out their rightful owners and ultimately found them.

She believed they come to us at just the right point in our lives. They wait and wait and then they ambush us. Tell us all they know.

There was a woman called Winnie who was seduced by paperbacks, one after the next.

There was a woman who went each week to breathe in the dust of the Great Big Book Exchange. She went to the shop owned by the man with two plastic arms. She went to him, even though he expected customers to eventually return the books they bought from him. He expected them to adopt his credit system and to take part in the Great Big Book Exchange. Everything swirling in a great big current, swapped hand to hand, always moving, always flowing. But she was a woman who liked to keep her own books. To keep beside her every book she ever read.

There was a woman who browsed those shelves, and couldn't help but wonder over the man in charge. She couldn't help wondering about him with his two plastic arms. As she worked her way round his shop she darted the odd look at him and, every glimpse she got of those arms, it made her flinch. And Winnie wondered what he could do and what he could accomplish with those two smooth arms. She wondered if it was only from the elbows down that he was artificial. It was hard to tell with the sleeves of the checked shirts he favoured rolled up just so.

Pride and Prejudice. The Silence of the Lambs. Flowers in the Attic. Jaws.

She watched carefully at how he managed when he had to count out change on his counter and when he had to operate the clunky old till. Winnie stood in shame with her pile of books, her heart turning over in her chest, when he was forced to take them from her to check the scribbled prices on the inside covers. She held her shopping bag open for him, so he could drop them in. She blushed every time she came here, but she still came back.

Rich Man, Poor Man. Sophie's Choice. The Exorcist. Jane Eyre. The World is Full of Married Men.

There was a woman who couldn't help coming back again and again to the Great Big Book Exchange.

Gone with the Wind. Peyton Place. Great Expectations.

There was a woman who went out on a Saturday with her grandson, now a teenager. He was a bit old-fashioned. He didn't understand the kids in his class at school. He didn't know what they were talking about.

Brideshead. Dead Zone. Tin Drum. Dallas. Dune.

There was a woman who bemoaned her grandson's fate, but only to herself, inside her head. Poor lad. His parents dead, his grandma quiet, her head in a book, his granddad pissed and crazy. In a little town like this. Like he's too old for his generation. They like – what do they like? – burgers in buns and french fries and rap music and punk music and hanging around on the street of a night. Even in this small town. They cluster around the phone box in the market square. She's seen them. Her grandson would never dream of knocking about with them.

What does he like? He likes the suety puddings and the mashed swede and the roast potatoes and jam roly-poly she makes for him. He's heftier, more careful, slower than his peers. He's sedentary. He reads.

A Clockwork Orange. Stig of the Dump. The Ghost of Thomas Kempe. Lolita.

He doesn't want a girlfriend. You don't want a girlfriend, do you? They take all your money off you. Girls your age are older than you. More mature. They'll be after all your money you've saved. Your inheritance. They'll take a lend of you. Leave you with nowt.

A Confederacy of Dunces. On the Road. The Naked Lunch. Battlestar Galactica.

There was a woman who was pleased her grandson had caught this reading bug of hers. She was glad he would come to choose books with her at the Great Big Book Exchange. Often they were the only customers in there on Saturday afternoons, making their way along their separate shelves.

They both loved the bare boards and dusty windows of the Exchange. They both loved getting off the bus and walking down the main road, where it was all fast food places and warehouse furniture stores. They both loved making their way to their favourite shop, tense with anticipation. Both knowing that the stock would have changed since the previous Saturday. In the days between, all the books would have jumped out of their homes and changed and switched about. That was why the shop was so dusty. Why the air was filled with motes of unsettled dirt and air and flakes of skin. Because of all the activity, the traffic, the exchanging going on. Always something new to read. Something you've never heard of. Something you always meant to read.

The two of them could sense this, walking down the main street towards the shop, which was lit and waiting. The man behind the counter had his jazz records playing. He was tapping his glass-topped desk with both plastic arms, almost jauntily.

There was a woman who didn't care what her grandson read. Let him take anything he wanted. It was all there for the choosing. How was she meant to know what was suitable or good?

He was working his way through the stacks. She'd watch him searching, all confident. He was ferreting about. He would hoik and hoard up books in his arms, snatch things out into the air with small grunts of surprise, of pleasure.

There was a woman who watched the line of golden light under her grandson's bedroom door at night. She was pleased he was burning electricity, all hours of the night. She knew his granddad would be cross if he saw the light burning. She was proud of the boy, though, when he arrived each morning, all panda-eyed at breakfast. Not wanting porridge, not wanting eggs. Wanting Gatsby. Wanting Jude the Obscure. Wanting The Dark is Rising, Salem's Lot.

There was a woman who wished she could read in her bed all night, too. She wanted to read till her eyes were smarting and flicking involuntarily from side to side. She wanted to fall asleep reading, and let the words decant themselves into her head.

The old man was suspicious. The house was too quiet. He didn't hold with reading that much. It sent people funny. He'd seen such things before.

The Guardians, The Mallens, The Midwich Cuckoos, The End of the Affair.

How long before the boy went all Camus and Kafka? How long before he got all disenchanted? Because this is what books would bring you: bother.

Catch-22. A Farewell to Arms. Doctor Who and the Daemons. Books gave you ideas.

This the old man knew. In his wisdom. His long years. Navy. Steelworks. Factory. His seeing the world. Knowing better than some old wife and a soft-headed grandson. Heads in books. No real clue about the world out there. The old man, embittered, cadaverous, sucking on Woodbines, barley sugars, tutting at the dust mites, the expense, the pensive silence of their house...

This the old man knew. All the big mouths he'd ever known, those thinking they were better than him, those thinking themselves above their station, all of them were tied up in books. Blokes in bunks in the bowels of ships. Union blokes pointing to paragraphs in books to back up their points. All of them rabble rousers or depressives. None of them really happy in themselves.

Or nancies, of course. That's where books led, too. He'd looked at the books in the boy's room and they made him tut and shake his head. They weren't the sort of thing a boy should read. Girls' books. Women's books. Not men's stories. Not at all. If men liked anything at all, men liked proper page-turning thrillers. Maybe war, maybe science fiction. Not this kind of stuff the boy went in for. Men didn't like mushy stuff.

Not this. Not Emma nor Maurice nor Orlando nor the Stud nor the Bitch nor Evelina nor Pamela nor Our Kate nor nowt.

There was a woman who slept perched high up on an old brass bed with her cadaverous old man and she wished and wished he'd let her put her bedside lamp on. She longed not for some secret demon lover, but just a little illumination through the wee small hours. But the old man wouldn't have it. The merest spill of light on his closed lids would plague him and spoil his rest – which he deserved; which she wasn't to ruin.

There was a woman who lay in the dark, full of resentment, seething on the rock hard mattress, hating everyone. Watching words blurring past on the underside of her eyelids – too fast to read, too fast to notice.

Her old man beside her, getting a proper night's sleep, was hating her in return. Hating her for even suggesting she bring her dirty old books in here, into their room, into their marital bed. The very thought gave him the horrors. He couldn't see how it was sanitary. Books were full of mites and lice and he would imagine them creeping out of the spines of her books, marching in formation down the snowy scoop of the duvet, across the old woman's ample lap... straight over him, into the luxuriant grey hairs of his nostrils, his earholes, the parched crevices of the rest of him... Contaminated in his own bed! By dirt and germs and his old woman's dirty books! And him who slept in the bowels of ships in hammocks during the war with a hundred other men! If he can't have a nice clean bed now in his extreme old age then that just wasn't good enough!

Her old man beside her knows that she feigns sleep and, when she thinks he doesn't notice, she gets up and creeps heavy-limbed onto the landing in her voluminous night gown. She sneaks and creaks past the bookcases on the top landing, past the piles of books on the stairs, on the sill of the hall window, by the cases in the downstairs hall, to the front room. There she sits by the gas fire for the balance of the night, till the sun comes over the terraces opposite and floods through the double-glazing, the net curtains, making her blink and look up from whatever it is she's reading. Dirtying her fingers with smudgy pages that others have pored over. Wearing out her eyes just to get to another last page. Another birth, death, marriage. Another anti-climax or a cliffhanger. Another unresolved The End.

She likes to finish her books by Saturday, so she's ready for her trip to the Great Big Book Exchange. All of this her old man knows. He knows more about her habits than she thinks.

There was an old woman who was learning to give away the books she read. To exchange them back, to take new ones. She was learning to live without them hoarded around her.

A Farewell to Arms! There was once a woman who made herself blush bright red, taking that particular book to the counter of the Great Big Book Exchange...

There was a woman who stammered and blushed as the man with no arms took it in his stride. He'd heard all the jokes and barbs and jibes before. And he never thought for a second his best customer would deliberately hurt his feelings.

(She didn't know it, but he sneaked messages into certain paperbacks, hoping she would buy them. He underlined certain lines. Certain phrases. Some of them, perhaps, innocuous by themselves. But to the close reader, perhaps, they would add up to a set of secret messages. If she was looking for them. If she looked in the right place. He didn't want to push his point of view. Didn't want to wave it under her nose. He trusted the power of love. The charm of a secret cipher. Above all, he trusted a reader of novels. He knew how one novel led to another and how, sooner or later, she would pick up the books that lay in wait for her. She would pick up his secret messages. And maybe he didn't mean them after all. Maybe it was just a game. Maybe his code was far too difficult to crack. In this way he hedged his bets. And the two of them never spoke about it. His Saturday girl knew all about it, though. And so did the grandson, who often read the novels that Winnie had finished. These two young people found the underlined sentences. They saw that they joined up to form a message. And they started to think, as any reader does, with utter selfishness, that the messages were addressed to themselves. Winnie was far too modest to think any such thing.)

The man with the two strong, plastic arms wished that his arms were real. He wished they were more flexible. He wished they had more feeling in them.

He was well-adjusted and he was resigned to his semi-artificial lot. But it would still be GOOD it would still be BETTER it would still be LOTS OF FUN if he was able to do the following with TWO REAL ARMS AGAIN:

1. Take hold of a woman properly. He meant, of course, in a nice, sexy, loving way, of course. He would hold her in a dancing cheek to cheek sort of a way, with the lights in his small sitting room turned low. They'd dance with just the pale light of the cinema across the road coming through the Venetian blinds. His arms would rest lightly – and full of feeling – against her warm back.

2. Heat up his favourite Heinz ravioli at lunch time and be able to stir the orangey parcels in the pan with his spatula without burning any. Tricky with no feeling in your hands!

3. Turn pages of novels without ripping any.

4. Do his underlinings as easily, as neatly, with as much surreptitious aplomb as he likes. Oh, his mind can find the loaded sentence, the sweetest sentiments, the most delicate hints, and double entendres, but he isn't always great at underlining things. Sometimes he's crossed words out inadvertently, trying to guide his pen. Fancy! Crossing things out when he was trying to draw attention to them!

That's how two plastic arms can make you feel, though! Clumsy! Destructive! The spoiler of all you desire!

Sometimes he was quite carried away by the romance of himself. The quiet, tidy, invisible excitement of being him. Watching which novels Winnie took away with her. Playing Ella Fitzgerald on his record player. Spending whole days in his dusty shop. Sipping smokey coffee and waiting for her to arrive.

Once there was a woman who appreciated everything about him and everything he did. She thought both he and his shop were magic. She'd have crawled on broken glass to get there on a Saturday afternoon. She said that, once.

Luckily, all she had to do was take the bus.

This is what you do to get around the place. In this county you have to take the bus everywhere. It's how the world works, and if you don't know how the buses work, well, then you've had it.

Once there was a woman and her grandson and they had the bus timetables round their way off by heart. The grandson was well-nigh hopeless with facts and dates and formulae for schoolwork, but he knew the times and stops for the double deckers and coaches, the Expresses, the Road Rangers. He knew when and where he was with the X50, the 213 and the 723.

Maybe he should be thinking of learning to drive himself, maybe having a little car of his own. He's nearly seventeen now and he could learn. He could have a runabout that he could use to get their shopping in. They could go to Asda and load up a whole week's worth of messages at once. But he has no faith in his ability to learn. His gran knows he'd be too timid and stopping at every unexpected thing. He'd be letting them all go past him. Letting every other driver push past. He wouldn't be forceful or sure enough.

Look at it this way. This place is best seen from the steamy windows of the bus. It might take a bit longer, getting place to place, but you do see life! You see all sorts!

There was a woman and her grandson and they'd been round all the nearby towns on the buses on Saturdays. These were their trips out. Sitting on the tartan seats, keeping themselves to theirselves, holding their brown paper bags of novels on their laps. Up and down the hills on long journeys on B-roads, through closed down towns and villages and estates. They'd clambered off in bus stations reeking of fumes and red hot chips. They'd gone straight away to share a pot of tea in the cafe in the marketplace. Scalding it down before going off to check out their favourite places for books. Cancer, Heart Foundation, Animal Rescue, Spastics.

There was a woman who wondered how people could simply toss their books away. Did they think that books became useless once read? Used up? Or did they think the story stayed trapped safely inside their heads?

There was a woman who knew that the stories gradually leaked away.

There was a woman whose favourite shop wasn't the Cancer or the Spastics. It was the Great Big Book Exchange and only the man there, the man with the two plastic hands, could gently coerce her into giving books back. Only with him did she see the sense in parting with books. It was part of the bargain. She got to take part in the great big exchange. Only if she brought them back. And really, she'd have said or done anything, anything, to come back to his shop each Saturday, again, again.

About the writers

Maureen Almond

Maureen Almond has lived in the North East all her life. She is a working writer experienced at teaching both children and adults. She has had three collections of poetry published, two of which have been included on the reading list for 'The Reception of Classical Literature in twentieth-century Poetry in English' at Oxford University. She won a New Writing North Time to Write Award in 2003.
For more information, see www.maureenalmond.com.

Peter Armstrong

Born in 1957 in Blaydon-on-Tyne, Peter Armstrong read philosophy and English at Sunderland Polytechnic before training as a psychiatric nurse and subsequently as a cognitive therapist. He works as an NHS clinician and trainer in Newcastle and lives in Tynedale. He had poems included in *Ten North East Poets* (Bloodaxe) and won an Eric Gregory Award. He has published three collections: *Risings* (Enitharmon), *The Red-Funnelled Boat* and *The Capital of Nowhere* (both Picador).

Neil Astley

Neil Astley has published two novels, *The End of My Tether* (Flambard, 2002; Scribner, 2003), which was shortlisted for the Whitbread First Novel Award, and *The Sheep Who Changed the World* (Flambard, 2005), as well as two poetry collections, *Darwin Survivor* (1988), a Poetry Book Society Recommendation, and *Biting My Tongue* (1995). He founded Bloodaxe Books in 1978 and has edited over 800 poetry books for Bloodaxe and several anthologies, including *Staying Alive* (2002), *Being Alive* (2004) and *Passionfood* (2005). He lives in the Tarset valley in Northumberland.

Bob Beagrie

Bob Beagrie lives in Middlesbrough. He works as a freelance writer and creative writing tutor. He won the Biscuit Poetry Prize in 2002 and was awarded a New Writing North Time to Write Award in 2003. He co-edits publisher Ek Zuban and edits the magazine *Kenaz*. Previous poetry publications include *Endeavour: Newfound Notes* (Biscuit

2004), *Huggin & Munnin* (Biscuit, 2002), *Masque: The Art of the Vampire* (Mudfog, 2000) and *Gothic Horror* (Mudfog, 1997). He has worked with Three Over Eden theatre company on the adaptations of his poems.

Andy Croft

Andy Croft's books include *Red Letter Days*, *Out of the Old Earth*, *A Weapon in the Struggle*, *Selected Poems of Randall Swingler*, *Comrade Heart*, *Red Sky at Night* (with Adrian Mitchell); six books of poetry – *Nowhere Special*, *Gaps Between Hills*, *Headland*, *Just as Blue*, *Great North* and *Comrade Laughter* – and 36 books for teenagers (mostly about football). Writing residencies include the Great North Run and HMP Holme House, Stockton. He lives in Middlesbrough.

Andrew Crumey

Andrew Crumey was born in Scotland and has lived in Newcastle upon Tyne for more than a decade. His latest novel, *Mobius Dick*, was published in 2004 to universal critical claim and became a bestseller. Waterstones chose it for their 'alternative Booker shortlist' and according to the *Independent on Sunday*, it was an "absolute sin that this book didn't win the Man Booker Prize". Andrew's previous four novels have been translated into many languages. He has a PhD in theoretical physics from Imperial College and is currently literary editor of *Scotland on Sunday*.

Barrie Darke

Barrie Darke was born and brought up in Newcastle and is a graduate of the MA in creative writing at Northumbria University. His novel *Black Sky At Night* won a Northern Promise Award from New Writing North in 2002. Recently, two short stories were shortlisted in the 10th Real Writers Awards. As a playwright, he is currently completing commissioned work for Paines Plough, Live Theatre and Theatre Cap-a-Pie. He also works as a tutor of creative writing.

Julia Darling

Julia Darling died in 2005. She was a poet, novelist and playwright and a pivotal writer of the North East literary scene. She published two novels, *Crocodile Soup* and *The Taxi Driver's Daughter* (both Penguin) and two acclaimed collections of poetry, *Sudden Collapses in Public Places* and *Apologies for Absence* (both ARC). Her collected plays for radio and the stage, *Eating the Elephant and Other Plays,* was published in 2005 by New Writing North.

For more information, see www.juliadarling.co.uk.

Fadia Faqir

Fadia Faqir is a Jordanian/British writer living in Durham city. Her first novel, *Nisanit,* was published by Penguin. Her second novel, *Pillars of Salt,* was published by Quartet Books. She is the editor and co-translator of *In the House of Silence: Autobiographical essays by Arab Women Writers* (Garnet Publishing). She has written a few short stories and plays, some of which will be published in the USA in 2006. Her third novel, *Sniffing Falafel,* is forthcoming.

For more information, see www.fadiafaqir.com.

Charles Fernyhough

Charles Fernyhough was born in Essex in 1968 and moved to County Durham in 1997. His first novel, *The Auctioneer,* was published by Fourth Estate in 1999. An extract from a work-in-progress appeared in *New Writing 11.* He is a part-time lecturer in psychology at the University of Durham and contributes to the MA in creative writing at Newcastle University.

For more information, see www.charlesfernyhough.com.

Chrissie Glazebrook

Chrissie Glazebrook is a novelist, short-story writer and journalist. Her writing has been described by the press as "brutally funny", "black humour at its finest", "anarchic black comedy", "subversively funny", "pithy, pungent, witty and wonderful". *The Sunday Times* described her "hot, anarchic humour", adding that "the author is brilliantly funny". Her novels are *The Madolescents* and *Blue Spark Sisters* (Heinemann and Arrow) and she is currently working on a third.

WN Herbert

Bill Herbert is published by Bloodaxe Books, with whom he has published four books, most recently *The Big Bumper Book of Troy.* He teaches creative writing at Newcastle University. His next book of poems will be *Bad Shaman Blues.*

Joan Hewitt

Joan Hewitt has an MA in writing poetry from Newcastle University. In 2003 she won the Waterhouse Poetry Prize from New Writing North. Her work has been successful in a number of poetry competitions – Ledbury Festival (2003), *Mslexia* (2004) and Kent and Sussex (2005). Her poems have featured in many publications, including *London Magazine, 100 Island Poems of Great Britain and Ireland* (Iron Press, 2005) and the forthcoming *Poetry and Sexuality* (Stirling University).

Paul Magrs

Paul Magrs was born in Jarrow in 1969. His first novel, *Marked for Life*, came out in 1995; his most recent is *To the Devil – a Diva!* He has written novels for children, teens, adults and Doctor Who fans. His next book is *Exchange*, which grew out of the story commissioned by New Writing North and published here.

Sara Maitland

Sara Maitland was born in 1950. Her first novel, *Daughter of Jerusalem*, won the Somerset Maugham Award in 1979. Her latest book is *On Becoming a Fairy Godmother* (Maia Press, 2003), a collection of (mainly) magical realist tales. She is also a feminist theologian with a particular interest in the meeting points of mysticism and madness. She is presently working on a history of silence.

Val McDermid

Scots-born Val McDermid has published 19 novels, one non-fiction book and a collection of short stories, *Stranded* (Flambard). Her work has been translated into over 30 languages and she has won many awards, including the Gold Dagger, the *Los Angeles Times* Book Prize, Icons of Scotland and the Anthony. A former journalist, she has been a full-time writer since 1991. Val divides her time between Northumberland and Manchester.

John Murray

John Murray was born in Cumbria in 1950. He has published seven novels and a collection of stories, *Pleasure*, which won the Dylan Thomas Award in 1988. He was longlisted for the Booker Prize with *Jazz Etc* (Flambard) in 2003.

Sean O'Brien

Sean O'Brien is a poet, critic, playwright, broadcaster, anthologist and editor. He is Professor of Poetry at Sheffield Hallam University and teaches on the writing MA there. His five collections of poetry have all won awards, most recently *Downriver* (Picador, 2001), which won the Forward Prize for best collection. In 2002, *Cousin Coat: Selected Poems 1976-2001* was published. His new verse version of Dante's *Inferno* will be published by Picador in 2006.

Ellen Phethean

Ellen Phethean is a sound artist, poet, playwright and editor. Her poetry is in *Sauce* (Bloodaxe Books) and has been broadcast on BBC Radio 3 and Radio 4. She co-founded Diamond Twig press with Julia Darling. She's written plays for radio, Northumbria University, Live Theatre's Youth Group and for schools. She recently created a sound installation for the Sage Gateshead's *Voices of The River's Edge Festival* in July 2005.

Jacob Polley

Jacob Polley was born in Carlisle, in 1975. He won an Eric Gregory Award in 2002. His first book of poems, *The Brink*, was a Poetry Book Society Choice and was short-listed for the TS Eliot, John Llewellyn Rhys and Forward prizes. He was selected as one of the 'Next Generation' poets in 2004. He also co-wrote the short film *Flickerman and the Ivory-skinned Woman*, which was filmed in 2002 and continues to be shown, most recently at the ICA. He is Fellow Commoner in the Arts at Trinity College, Cambridge, 2005-07.

Angela Readman

Angela Readman's work has appeared in *Mslexia*, *London Magazine* and *Envoi*, and the anthologies *Smelter* and *Flesh of the Bear* (a bi-lingual anthology of Finnish and English poets from Ek Zuban). She was included in *Unholy Trinity* (as Angel Readman), a trilogy of new women poets, and *Colors/Colours* was published by Diamond Twig in 2001. In 2004 she won The Biscuit Poetry Competition and produced a full-length collection *Sex with Elvis*. She is currently the editor of *Newcastle Stories*.

Wendy Robertson

Wendy Robertson has lived and worked in the North East since she was nine. After a career in higher education, she now writes full-time, focusing mostly on long fiction, although she has written and published short stories, newspaper pieces, reviews and magazine articles. She takes the recent history, the topography and the people of south Durham as a starting point for her fiction. Her novel, *A Woman Scorned*, about a notorious murder case, is now out in paperback. Her new novel, *No Rest For The Wicked,* about a travelling theatre, was published in September 2005.
For more information, see www.wendyrobertson.com.

Mark Robinson

Mark Robinson has a shadowy day-time existence as something senior at Arts Council England North East, as well as being a writer and performer. His published poetry collections include *The Horse Burning Park, Gaps Between Hills* and *Half A Mind.* He has also edited numerous anthologies and a collection of essays on poetry readings, *Words Out Loud.* He lives in Eaglescliffe near Stockton-on-Tees.

Paul Summers

Paul Summers was born in Blyth, Northumberland, in 1967. He now lives in North Shields. He was founding editor of leftfield magazines *Billy Liar* and *Liar Republic.* His poetry collections include *The Last Bus* (1998), *Cunawabi* (2002) and *Big Bella's Dirty Café,* which is to be published in late 2005. He has also written for theatre, TV and film, as well as collaborating with many artists on mixed media pieces. *Home (in 3 bits),* a music/spoken word collaboration with former Lindisfarne member Dave Hull-Denholm, is also due for release in autumn 2005.

Fiona Ritchie Walker

Fiona Ritchie Walker is originally from Montrose, Scotland, but has lived in the North East since the early 1990s. She has two poetry collections: *Lip Reading* (Diamond Twig) and *Garibaldi's Legs* (Iron Press). A Northern Promise Award from New Writing North in 2004 helped develop her short story writing and her work features in several publications including *Newcastle Stories 1, Bracket* and *Ellipsis 2* (Comma Press). For more information, see www.fionaritchiewalker.co.uk.

Anna Woodford

Anna Woodford has received an Eric Gregory Award, an Arvon/Jerwood Apprenticeship, a Hawthornden Fellowship and a residency at the Blue Mountain Center (New York). Her poems and reviews have appeared in the *TLS*, *Poetry London* and *Poetry Ireland Review*. She recently completed a commission for the Arts Council, writing poems to be projected onto fire stations in the North East. She will be teaching 'Writing from the Inside Out' at the Centre for Lifelong Learning, Newcastle, during 2005/06.

Other work by North East writers

Bound by Wendy Robertson, Charles Fernyhough, Fadia Faqir, Sara Maitland and Paul Magrs (2004)

Bound is a collection of short stories written by writers who live and work in County Durham. The book seeks to explore the creative impulses of the Durham environment. Five writers were commissioned to use the short story form to explore these ideas and to write an essay which explored their relationship to County Durham as writers. The writers – Wendy Robertson, Charles Fernyhough, Fadia Faqir, Sara Maitland and Paul Magrs – all have different reasons for coming to live or work in County Durham. Some were born in the North East, others moved here to live and work; they have different attachments to Durham and different experiences of the place. The book itself is also a work of art. Designed by artist Tanya Axford in conjunction with designers Sumo, the *Bound* book also turns itself into a sculpture as you read it.

ISBN: 0-9541456-2-3
Price £8 (+ £3 P&P)

Eating the Elephant and Other Plays by Julia Darling (2005)

Eating the Elephant and Other Plays brings together plays for stage and radio from one of the North East's most enduring writers, Julia Darling, who died in 2005. This first collection of her plays includes *Eating the Elephant*, *Head of Steel*, *The Women Who Painted Ships*, *Venetia Love Goes Netting*, *The Last Post*, *Personal Belongings*, *Doughnuts Like Fanny's* and *Attachments* and her radio plays, *Sea Life*, *Posties* and *Appointments*. Each play is introduced by the author.

ISBN 0-9541456-4-X
Price: £14.99 (+ £3 P&P)

Kaput! by **Margaret Wilkinson** (2004)

A Russian artist with his eye on posterity is having a helluva party in his lakeside dacha but there's blood on the floor. A hundred years later, an American housewife with bad dreams believes her husband's a murderer. Meanwhile two fugitives – a naked stranger and a bruised Madonna – meet in a dark wood to exchange lives across centuries and continents. A play by Margaret Wilkinson, inspired by the short stories of Anton Chekhov and Raymond Carver.

ISBN 0-9541456-3-1
Price: £5 (+ £2 P&P)

Tongues in Trees by **Maureen Almond** (2005)

A collection of poems commemorating the trees condemned during the period of poet Maureen Almond's writing residency at Darlington's North Lodge Park. All proceeds from the sale of this book will be given to The Friends of North Lodge Park so that they can purchase replacement trees.

ISBN 0-9541456-8-2
Price £1 (+ £1 P&P)

We Love You, Arthur by **Fiona Evans** (2005)

We Love you Arthur, a play by Fiona Evans, tells the story of Julie and Lisa, two girls coming of age in a community being torn apart. Growing up is never easy, especially in Easington Colliery during 1984. Achieving big hair can be problem, but how can you ever look like Cyndi Lauper when your dad's out on strike and you can't afford food, never mind a can of extra-hold, perm-welding Elnett?

ISBN 0-9541456-6-6
Price: £5 (+ £2 P&P)

To order any of these titles, ring New Writing North on 0191 4888 580 or email Holly Hooper at holly@newwritingnorth.com.